THE ILLUSTRATED GUIDE TO
CRIMINAL LAW

WRITTEN & ILLUSTRATED BY

NATHANIEL BURNEY

See more online at
lawcomic.net
thecriminallawyer.tumblr.com

Published by
Jones McClure Publishing
P.O. Box 3348
Houston TX 77253-3348
www.JonesMcClure.com
1-800-OCONNOR (626-6667)

Printed December 2012 in the U.S.A.

ISBN 978-1-59839183-1

TO CRIME!

CONTENTS

"YOU KNOW, AN UNDERCOVER HAS TO TELL YOU IF HE'S A COP. OTHERWISE IT'S ENTRAPMENT."

No. That's just *not true*, and it only takes a little thought to see why. But it's repeated on street corners, in locker rooms, and on websites every day. And it's just one of many popular *myths* about criminal law. There are all these ideas floating around out there about self-defense, accomplice liability, entrapment, etc., that are completely wrong.

This book started out as an attempt to *debunk* those myths. Maybe explain some basic principles of criminal law. Stuff that should have been covered in an eighth-grade civics class, except they don't seem to teach that anymore.

And I wanted to do it in a way that was more accessible to a high school kid than my wordy and obscure law blog. My goal was to break it all down into easy pieces, start from first principles, and explain it as casually as possible. Doodle some pictures and stories to make these amorphous concepts more concrete. Make it fun.

I knew that almost nobody would see it, but at least it would be out there.

The reaction blew my mind. These little doodles got very popular, very fast. (When I realized that people were actually reading it, I did make an effort to draw better — or at least more consistently.) Law professors and students wrote to ask when the book was coming out. That was another surprise: I hadn't thought of them as an audience, nor of this ever becoming a book.

But a book it became. And it actually covers a lot of the same material as a first-year law school class on criminal law. Except I've gone out of my way not to cite statutes and case names wherever possible — they don't really add anything to the discussion, and often distract. Plus, not adhering to actual cases lets me make up my own facts to better explain the concepts.

And now here it is, a real book. I hope you have as much fun reading this as I've had writing it. With any luck, these scribbles will help someone out there understand how the law works. Meanwhile, I'll be working on the next book, on criminal procedure — talk about myths that need debunking!

Enjoy!

Nathan

IGNORANCE OF THE LAW IS NO EXCUSE.

— Every prosecutor who ever
wanted to hold someone culpable.

Though most people who managed to make their way from fourth grade to fifth are aware of the legal maxim, ignorance of the law remains rampant. Let's face facts: As there are now estimated to be more than 4,000 federal criminal laws, plus too many regulations to count that can result in criminal penalties, nobody "knows" the law anymore.

And yet, *ignorantia juris non excusat* (note the cool way I used the same phrase, but this time in Latin to show how I'm an erudite lawyer and speak the magic language of the law that prevents you, unschooled in such things, from being nearly as cool as I am) remains the rule, as anyone with the misfortune of rubbing their nose up against an unpleasant situation with a badged person will soon realize. Based on my nearly 30 years of experience as a criminal defense lawyer, and my over five years of experience as a law blogger fielding comments and questions from nonlawyers, I feel comfortable opining that ignorance of the law is pervasive.

Up to now, it was sadly understandable. To avoid being ignorant, your choices were limited to attending law school, which was at best a partial solution, or spending every waking moment reading court decisions, treatises, statutes, law review articles, and the occasional law blog. The prospects were decidedly unfun. Not only would you hate it after an hour or two, but it would not likely suffice, as you would still lack the specialized knowledge and experience necessary to parse the dense, confusing, and heavy prose. Your best effort, and most sincere purpose, would be more likely to make your head explode than give you sufficient knowledge to confidently proclaim that you are no longer ignorant of the law.

Nathan Burney has changed that. He's accomplished what was previously unthinkable by providing a comprehensive, clear, and accurate overview of American criminal law, but doing so in a way that's funny, engaging, and interesting.

Make no mistake, while it's alluringly illustrated and just a bit snarky, Nathan's work is as accurate and comprehensive as humanly possible. By definition, no one book can cover every nuance of criminal law, as it varies from jurisdiction to jurisdiction, and changes daily. But the fundamentals have remained in place for a couple hundred years, and Nathan has captured them, organized them, provided clear and concise examples of them, in a way no one has before.

Remarkably, crime and the law is one of those subjects that seem to perpetually fascinate people, even if they have an unreasonable belief that it will never directly impact their life. Consider such infamous cases as Orenthal James Simpson, or more recently, Casey Anthony. We love to watch their trials (and tribulations), and often get quite emotional about the outcome, whether because we agree or are outraged. We cry all the time about "injustice," whatever that happens to mean to us. Sometimes we shake our heads over it. Sometimes we seethe. Sometimes we take to the streets. Yet almost every time, we are long on feelings and short on knowledge. It's awfully hard to have a meaningful debate when none of the arguers have much of a clue what the law requires.

There is really no excuse for this pervasive ignorance any longer. After reading Nathan's *magnus illustratum* (see how I threw some Latin in again just to show off?), you will have a firm understanding of American criminal law. Indeed, you may well have a better grasp than most lawyers.

While it may not be sufficient to get you through the bar exam (though it will likely be more than adequate to ace any criminal law questions they throw at you), it will most assuredly give you a firm foundation with which to understand the criminal justice system. Whether for your own sake (and I hope not) or for the sake of others and discussion, the substance is sound, thorough, and comprehensive.

The worst part is that you will enjoy reading about criminal law. Whether you're a high schooler, law student, or street tough, Nathan's amazing ability to keep such otherwise leaden content moving, interesting, and (dare I say it) fun is extraordinary. Between the illustrations and examples, not only will you learn exactly what the law is about but you will have a hard time keeping a smile off your face.

The upshot is that there is no longer a reason why nonlawyers (which is another name for people too smart to spend three years of their lives under fluorescent lights so they can be the butt of a million really good jokes) should remain ignorant of the law. Given how critical a working knowledge of criminal law is in our lives and our society, there's no excuse for meandering through life without any idea whether your next step could land you in prison. From this point forward, ignorance of the law is a choice. Don't let it be yours.

– Scott Greenfield

"WHAT IS IT?"

FIRST, LET'S START OFF
WITH SOME BASICS:
CRIMINAL LAW IS ABOUT **CRIME**.

THAT'S PRETTY BASIC.

BUT WHAT **IS** CRIME,
ANYWAY?

WELL...

CRIME IS SOMETHING
YOU'RE NOT **SUPPOSED**
TO DO... BUT THERE'S
MORE TO IT THAN THAT.

CHEATING ON YOUR
BOYFRIEND MIGHT BE
WRONG, BUT IT'S
NOT A **CRIME**.

CRIME IS SOMETHING MORE THAN MERELY RUDE,
IMPROPER, OR OBJECTIONABLE BEHAVIOR.
IT'S SOMETHING SOCIETY HAS PROHIBITED
AS A MATTER OF **LAW**. ...BUT IT'S NOT SIMPLY
STUFF THAT'S AGAINST THE LAW, EITHER.

IF YOU FIRE SOMEONE FOR BEING IRISH, YOU COULD BE SUED FOR DISCRIMINATION, BUT YOU WON'T GO TO JAIL FOR IT.

NO.

"*CRIME*" MEANS THOSE ACTS THAT ARE SO *WRONG*... SO *BAD*... SO *DANGEROUS*... THAT SOCIETY *PUNISHES* THOSE WHO DO THEM.

BUT NOT THROUGH MOB VIOLENCE OR SOCIAL DISAPPROBATION.

CRIMINAL PUNISHMENT IS NOT IMPOSED BY PRIVATE CITIZENS, INFORMAL GROUPS, OR ONE'S SOCIAL CIRCLE.

CRIMINAL PUNISHMENT IS IMPOSED BY THE *STATE*.*

*PICTURED HERE IS A SORT OF MODERN ATHENA/ROMA.

FORGET HOBBES'S LEVIATHAN OR UNCLE SAM... THE ANCIENTS HAD IT RIGHT WHEN THEY PERSONIFIED GOVERNMENT AS A BADASS CHICK.

YOU DON'T WANT TO GET ON HER BAD SIDE.

SO CRIME MEANS AN ACT, DEEMED UNACCEPTABLE BY SOCIETY, THAT'S SO BAD THAT THE STATE WILL STEP IN AND *PUNISH* YOU FOR DOING IT.

BUT WHAT DO WE MEAN BY "PUNISHMENT"? WHAT IS IT, AND WHY DOES IT HAPPEN?

WE'LL COVER THAT NEXT...

"TAKE THAT!"

ONE OF THE STATE'S FUNCTIONS IS TO DEAL WITH CRIME. IN THIS ROLE, THE STATE IS A LITTLE LIKE A **MOTHER**...

LIKE A WHAT, NOW?

LIKE A MOTHER, SHE HAS TO **PROTECT** US FROM THREATS, **TEACH** US RIGHT FROM WRONG, AND **CORRECT** US WHENEVER WE OURSELVES DO WRONG.

A REAL MOTHER HAS LOTS OF TOOLS TO DO ALL OF THAT, AND MORE.

BUT THE STATE ONLY HAS **ONE** TOOL, REALLY...

AND IT'S A BIG FREAKIN' **HAMMER!**

WE CALL THIS HAMMER **"PUNISHMENT."**

PUNISHMENT IS WHEN THE STATE **HURTS** YOU.

PAIN AND SIMPLE.

THERE ARE VARIOUS WAYS THE STATE CAN HURT YOU, BUT THEY ALL BOIL DOWN TO...

| INFLICTING **PAIN** | TAKING YOUR **PROPERTY** | HARMING YOUR **REPUTATION** | RESTRICTING YOUR **LIBERTY** |

AT ITS MOST EXTREME, THE STATE DOES ALL OF THE ABOVE BY TAKING YOUR **LIFE.**

IT'S A HELL OF A THING... KILLING A MAN.

WITHIN THESE CATEGORIES,
THERE ARE A VARIETY OF DIFFERENT WAYS
THE STATE CAN IMPOSE EACH TYPE OF
PUNISHMENT, RANGING FROM...

 "PROVE YOU WON'T
GET IN TROUBLE AGAIN"
THINGS LIKE PAROLE,
PROBATION, CONDITIONAL
DISMISSALS, ETC.

TO THINGS LIKE
FINES AND
COMMUNITY
SERVICE,

 TO REHABILITATIVE
REPROGRAMMING,

TO INCARCERATION,
EXILE, TORTURE,
AND DEATH.

SO THAT IS BASICALLY WHAT PUNISHMENT *IS*.
BUT **WHY** DOES THE STATE IMPOSE PUNISHMENT IN
THE FIRST PLACE? YOU MIGHT BE SURPRISED.

LET'S EXPLORE THAT NOW...

"FOR THE LOVE OF GOD, *WHY*?"

LET'S SAY YOU COMMITTED A CRIME, HARMING SOCIETY.

THE STATE RESPONDS BY HARMING *YOU*.

IT'S REASONABLE TO ASK YOURSELF...

WHY?

WHAT POSSIBLE *PURPOSE* IS SERVED BY THE STATE ADDING INJURY TO INJURY?

HOW DOES ADDING *MORE* SUFFERING MAKE SOCIETY ANY BETTER OFF?

THERE ARE SEVERAL IDEAS. LET'S START WITH THE MOST "CIVILIZED" PURPOSE OF PUNISHMENT:

REHABILITATION

SOME CRIMES ARE CAUSED BY PROBLEMS THAT MIGHT BE **CORRECTED** — BEHAVIORAL OR PSYCHOLOGICAL DYSFUNCTION, ADDICTION, ECONOMIC AND COMMUNITY PRESSURES, OR EVEN SHEER IGNORANCE.

MERELY THROWING SUCH OFFENDERS IN JAIL, WITHOUT FIXING THE UNDERLYING PROBLEM, SEEMS AN AWFUL WASTE.

IT DOESN'T SOLVE ANYTHING.

SO WHY NOT USE THE STATE'S MIGHT TO **CHANGE** THE OFFENDER, SO HE WON'T BE LIKELY TO DO IT AGAIN?

A NICE IDEA, BUT IT ONLY WORKS IN UNUSUAL CASES.

FOR ONE THING, MOST OFFENDERS DON'T **NEED** TO BE REHABILITATED. STUDIES VARY, BUT OUT OF EVERY 100 PEOPLE WHO GET ARRESTED, ROUGHLY 83 OF THEM NEVER WILL AGAIN. THEIR **FIRST** CONTACT WITH THE CRIMINAL JUSTICE SYSTEM IS THEIR **LAST.**

MOST ARE OTHERWISE LAW-ABIDING PEOPLE WHO EITHER MADE A FOOLISH MISTAKE OR WERE IN A ONE-OFF SITUATION THAT WILL NEVER ARISE AGAIN.

PUNISHMENT IS **UNNECESSARY** TO REHABILITATE THEM BECAUSE THERE'S NO CHARACTER FLAW TO REHABILITATE.

SOME OTHERS ARE SIMPLY SCARED STRAIGHT BY THE SHAME AND TRAUMA OF THE MERE ARREST ITSELF. NO PUNISHMENT IS NEEDED TO REHABILITATE THEM, EITHER.

BUT WHAT ABOUT THE REMAINING 17%, THE RECIDIVISTS WHO *DO* GET IN TROUBLE AGAIN?

YEAH, WHAT ABOUT US?

THESE ARE THE ONES REHABILITATION IS AIMED AT. ...WELL, SOME OF THEM, ANYWAY.

IN THE OLD DAYS, SOME THOUGHT THAT PRISON ALONE WAS ENOUGH. IT WAS TIME TO THINK ABOUT WHAT YOU HAD DONE, AND MEND YOUR WAYS.

SO HOW DID THAT WORK OUT FOR YA?

EVENTUALLY, REFORMERS RECOGNIZED THAT REAL CHANGE IS ONLY GOING TO HAPPEN IF THE OFFENDER HIMSELF *WANTS* TO CHANGE. AND EVEN THEN, MANY CAN'T SUCCEED WITHOUT HELP.

SO NOW, MANY SYSTEMS OFFER *PROGRAMS* THAT ARE DESIGNED TO HELP "CURE" OFFENDERS OF THE UNDERLYING CAUSES OF THEIR CRIMINAL BEHAVIOR.

SUCH PROGRAMS ARE STRICTLY VOLUNTARY, THOUGH ALL INVOLVE SOME LOSS OF LIBERTY.

THE STATE HAS TO **HURT** YOU IN ORDER TO **HELP** YOU, YOU SEE?

TOUGH LOVE, BABY!

PROGRAMS RANGE FROM GROUP THERAPY TO BOOT CAMPS, FROM ONE-HOUR VIDEOS ON THE RISKS OF MARIJUANA TO INPATIENT ADDICTION TREATMENT AND LIFESTYLE REEDUCATION THAT CAN LAST FOR **YEARS.**

USUALLY, THE GREATER THE STATE'S CONTROL OVER YOU, THE MORE LIKELY YOU'LL COME OUT WITH THE LONG-TERM BEHAVIOR CHANGES AND THE LIFE SKILLS NEEDED FOR TRUE REHABILITATION.

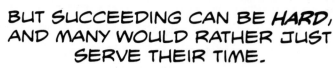

BUT SUCCEEDING CAN BE **HARD,** AND MANY WOULD RATHER JUST SERVE THEIR TIME.

ALSO, NOT EVERY CAUSE OF CRIME CAN BE "CURED."

NOT BY A LONG SHOT.

SO REHABILITATION CAN'T BE THE **ONLY** PURPOSE OF PUNISHMENT. AND IT ISN'T. THERE ARE SEVERAL.

(SOME MORE "CIVILIZED" THAN OTHERS.)

SO NOW LET'S TALK ABOUT DETERRENCE...

"DON'T DO THAT *AGAIN!*"

REHABILITATION IS THE "*ENLIGHTENED*" PURPOSE OF PUNISHMENT... FOR WHAT THAT'S WORTH.

IT'S GREAT WHEN IT *HAPPENS*, BUT MOST OF THE TIME REHABILITATION IS EITHER UNNECESSARY OR UNREALISTIC.

ALSO, IT'S NOT REALLY WHAT MOST PEOPLE *THINK* OF AS THE PURPOSE OF PUNISHMENT.

IF YOU WERE TO ASK A THOUGHTFUL PERSON *WHY* WE PUNISH CRIMINALS, HE WOULD BE MORE LIKELY TO SAY SOMETHING LIKE...

TO TEACH THEM A LESSON...

...AND SO OTHERS THINK TWICE BEFORE DOING THE SAME THING.

IN OTHER WORDS:
DETERRENCE

BY INFLICTING PUNISHMENT, THE STATE TRIES TO **DETER** YOU FROM COMMITTING THAT CRIME EVER AGAIN...

DON'T EVER DO THAT AGAIN!

(THIS IS "SPECIFIC" DETERRENCE.)

...AND ALSO TO DETER **OTHERS** FROM COMMITTING THAT CRIME AT ALL.

(THIS IS "GENERAL" DETERRENCE.)

THAT GOES FOR THE REST OF YOU, TOO!

LIKE REHABILITATION, DETERRENCE IS A FINE IDEA. IT'S FAIRLY CIVILIZED, AND IT SEEMS LIKE IT *OUGHT* TO WORK...

BUT *DOES* IT?

WELL, THAT DEPENDS.

DETERRENCE ONLY WORKS WHEN SOMEONE WHO *MIGHT* HAVE COMMITTED A CRIME CHOOSES INSTEAD *NOT* TO DO IT BECAUSE HE FEARS THAT HE MIGHT BE PUNISHED FOR IT.

hmmm...

IT'S IMPOSSIBLE TO MEASURE THE NUMBER OF CRIMES THAT *DIDN'T* HAPPEN, BUT IT DOESN'T TAKE MUCH THOUGHT TO SEE THAT THE NUMBER OF CRIMES PREVENTED BY DETERRENCE HAS TO BE FAIRLY *SMALL*.

FIRST OF ALL, THE VAST MAJORITY OF PEOPLE ARE DETERRED NOT BY THE THREAT OF PUNISHMENT, BUT BY THEIR OWN SENSE OF *RIGHT* AND *WRONG*.

AS FOR THE SMALL MINORITY WHO *DO* COMMIT CRIMES, HARDLY *ANY* GO THROUGH EVEN THE MOST RUDIMENTARY COST-BENEFIT ANALYSIS BEFOREHAND.

DETERRENCE IS ONLY A FACTOR WHEN SOMEONE CONSCIOUSLY WEIGHS THE PROS AND CONS OF COMMITTING A CRIME.

GET IT? CONs!

... CONVICTS?

... NEVER MIND.

CRIMES OF PASSION?
NO.

CRIMES OF DESPERATION?
NO.

WHAT ARE YOU _DOING_, JEAN VALJEAN?

CRIMES OF MISTAKE? NO.

I THOUGHT SHE WAS 21!

UNTHINKING CRIMES?
BY DEFINITION,
NO.

MANY CRIMES OF
OPPORTUNITY?

NO.

DETERRENCE ONLY MATTERS FOR CRIMES THAT WERE **PLANNED**, OR WHERE THERE WAS TIME (AND INCLINATION) TO **THINK**.

STILL, ONCE YOU RULE OUT TEENAGERS, ANGRY, EMOTIONAL, OR IRRATIONAL PEOPLE, THE HUNGRY OR ADDICTED, THE CLUELESS, AND THE SPUR-OF-THE-MOMENT...

THERE **ARE** A FEW CASES WHERE DETERRENCE **DOES** COME INTO PLAY.

LISTEN UP, HERE'S THE PLAN...

IN THOSE CASES WHERE DETERRENCE **COULD** WORK, HOW **DOES** IT WORK?

FOR BOTH SPECIFIC AND GENERAL DETERRENCE, THE **AMOUNT** OF PUNISHMENT MATTERS SURPRISINGLY LITTLE.

AFTER ALL, HOW MANY PEOPLE EVEN **KNOW** HOW MUCH TIME ANY PARTICULAR PERSON GOT FOR ANY PARTICULAR CRIME?

APART FROM CRIMINAL LAWYERS AND EXPERIENCED OFFENDERS, ALMOST **NOBODY** HAS ANY IDEA HOW MUCH PUNISHMENT THEY'RE ACTUALLY FACING, IF ANY.

WHAT MATTERS MOST INSTEAD IS THE THREAT THAT **SOME** PUNISHMENT WILL BE IMPOSED...

IN OTHER WORDS, IT'S THE **PERCEPTION** THAT ONE IS LIKELY TO BE PUNISHED (IF CAUGHT) THAT IS THE DETERRENT.

IN SENTENCING A TYPICAL OFFENDER TO, SAY, FIVE YEARS IN PRISON, THE GENERAL DETERRENCE THAT RESULTS IS BASICALLY **ZERO** BECAUSE ALMOST NOBODY WILL EVER KNOW ABOUT IT.

THE PERCEPTION THAT DRIVES **GENERAL** DETERRENCE COMES MERELY FROM ONE'S OVERALL **IMPRESSION** OF HOW LIKELY IT IS THAT, IN THIS COMMUNITY, THE GUILTY WILL BE CAUGHT AND THEN PUNISHED.

THIS IMPRESSION IS MORE LIKELY TO COME FROM **TV**, MOVIES, AND URBAN LEGEND THAN FROM ANY ACTUAL DATA.

MEANWHILE, THE *SPECIFIC* DETERRENCE OF GIVING JOHN DOE THOSE FIVE YEARS IS ALSO NEGLIGIBLE. THOSE WHO *ARE* DETERRED ARE NOT AFFECTED BY THE *LENGTH* OF THE SENTENCE AS MUCH AS THE DESIRE TO AVOID *ANY* SENTENCE IN THE FUTURE.

RECIDIVISTS, MEANWHILE, CHOOSE TO RE-OFFEND REGARDLESS OF THE SENTENCE THEY RECEIVED, OFTEN RATCHETING UP LONGER AND LONGER SENTENCES WITHOUT ANY APPARENT DETERRENT EFFECT.

SO REHABILITATION AND DETERRENCE MAY BE "CIVILIZED" PURPOSES OF PUNISHMENT, BUT THEIR REAL-LIFE APPLICABILITY IS *LIMITED*, AT BEST.

STILL, THERE ARE AT LEAST THREE MORE PURPOSES OF PUNISHMENT.

WE MAY NOT LIKE TO TALK ABOUT THEM, AND AT LEAST ONE IS SO UNCIVILIZED THAT YOU'LL PROBABLY NEVER HEAR IT MENTIONED IN COURT.

WE'RE GOING TO TALK ABOUT THEM NOW....

"THE THREE R's"

REHABILITATION AND DETERRENCE ARE WHAT WE LIKE TO THINK OF AS THE PURPOSES OF PUNISHMENT. BUT AS WE'VE SEEN, THAT'S NOT QUITE TRUE. THEY DON'T APPLY TO MOST CASES, AND EVEN THEN THEY DON'T ALWAYS WORK WELL.

BUT THERE IS ANOTHER PURPOSE OF PUNISHMENT THAT DOES WORK VERY WELL INDEED:

REMOVAL

(ALSO CALLED "INCAPACITATION" OR "PREVENTION").

"REMOVAL" MEANS JUST THAT: THE OFFENDER IS REMOVED FROM SOCIETY.

THIS PURPOSE DOESN'T CARE ABOUT REFORMING YOU OR MAKING YOU THINK TWICE. NO, THIS PURPOSE IS ALL ABOUT REMOVING A *DANGER* FROM OUR MIDST.

IF SOMEONE IS A THREAT TO PUBLIC **SAFETY**, WE PROTECT THE PUBLIC BY GETTING RID OF THE THREAT.

BETTER TO JUST KEEP HIM BEHIND BARS...

OR EXILE HIM...

OR KILL HIM...

...SO HE CANNOT HURT SOCIETY AGAIN.

ONCE AGAIN, HOWEVER, WE HAVE THE PROBLEM OF SPECIFIC SENTENCES FOR A GIVEN CRIME.

IF **REHABILITATION** IS THE PURPOSE, THEN THE SENTENCE SHOULD BE AS LONG AS IT TAKES FOR THE OFFENDER TO **TRANSFORM** INTO A LAW-ABIDING CITIZEN.

IF **DETERRENCE** IS THE PURPOSE, THEN THE LENGTH OF THE SENTENCE IS HARDLY RELEVANT, COMPARED TO THE MERE THREAT OF **SOME** PENALTY.

LIKEWISE, IF **REMOVAL** IS THE PURPOSE, THEN WHY RELEASE A KNOWN DANGER **BACK** INTO SOCIETY JUST BECAUSE HE'S SERVED HIS TIME?

IF WE WERE CONSISTENT WITH THESE OSTENSIBLY CIVILIZED REASONS FOR PUNISHMENT, IT WOULD NOT MAKE **SENSE** TO SAY "THIS CRIME WILL GET YOU FIVE YEARS IN PRISON."

INSTEAD, SUCH A "CIVILIZED" SENTENCE WOULD BE PURELY **INDEFINITE:** YOUR PUNISHMENT WOULD LAST UNTIL IT WASN'T NEEDED ANYMORE — POTENTIALLY LASTING **FOREVER.**

BUT THIS IS HARDLY A CIVILIZED THING TO DO. THAT'S THE STUFF OF **DUNGEONS** AND TYRANT'S GULAGS, NOT SOMETHING WE ASSOCIATE WITH MODERN **JUSTICE.**

INSTEAD, WE BASE THE SEVERITY OF YOUR PUNISHMENT ON THE SEVERITY OF YOUR **CRIME**.

STEALING A MILLION DOLLARS IS PUNISHED MORE SEVERELY THAN SHOPLIFTING.

20 YEARS STATE PRISON

20 HOURS COMMUNITY SERVICE

GIVING SOMEONE A BLACK EYE IS PUNISHED LESS SEVERELY THAN PUTTING HIM IN TRACTION.

INTENTIONALLY **MURDERING** ONE PERSON IS PUNISHED MORE SEVERELY THAN KILLING A FAMILY IN A CAR **ACCIDENT**.

THIS PROPORTIONALITY — THIS SENSE THAT PUNISHMENT MUST FIT THE CRIME — IS THE HALLMARK OF

RETRIBUTION.

THIS IS YOUR CLASSICAL "EYE FOR AN EYE" PURPOSE OF PUNISHMENT, AND IT'S WHAT MOST PEOPLE ARE THINKING OF WHEN THEY TALK ABOUT GETTING "*JUSTICE.*"

JUSTICE IS NOT ABOUT MAKING YOU NICER, OR DETERRING POTENTIAL ACTS IN THE FUTURE, OR EVEN ABOUT TAKING YOU OFF THE STREETS... IT'S ABOUT YOU GETTING WHAT YOU *DESERVED.*

YOU HURT SOMEONE — OR SOCIETY — SO YOU HAVE TO BE HURT ABOUT THE SAME AMOUNT TO MAKE EVERYTHING EVEN, TO RESTORE BALANCE, TO SATISFY A SENSE OF FAIRNESS.

SO WHEN YOU GET A FIVE-YEAR SENTENCE, THOSE FIVE YEARS ARE NOT CHOSEN BECAUSE THAT'S THE MAGIC NUMBER THAT WILL DETER OTHERS, MEND YOUR WAYS, OR KEEP US SAFE UNTIL YOU'RE NO THREAT.

THOSE FIVE YEARS ARE WHAT YOUR OFFENSE IS **WORTH.**

IF THE PUNISHMENT FITS THE CRIME, THEN EVERYONE FEELS LIKE JUSTICE WAS DONE. THERE'S AN INHERENT SENSE OF INJUSTICE WHEN SOMEONE'S SENTENCE IS TOO HARSH FOR WHAT HE DID (OR TOO LIGHT).

HE WON'T SUFFER LIKE OUR KIDS DID — IT'S NOT FAIR!

STILL...

EVEN THOUGH RETRIBUTION IS THE MOST **IMPORTANT** FACTOR IN CRIMINAL PUNISHMENT, NOBODY LIKES TO **ADMIT** IT.

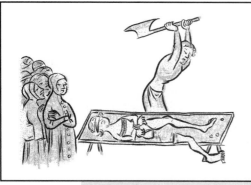

RESPONDING TO **PAIN** WITH MORE **PAIN**?

IT'S SO... SO **SADISTIC**...

SO **BARBARIC!**

HARDLY AN ENLIGHTENED PURPOSE OF PUNISHMENT.

BUT EVEN THOUGH WE DON'T LIKE TO TALK ABOUT RETRIBUTION, IN PRIVATE WE'LL AT LEAST ACKNOWLEDGE ITS IMPORTANCE.

THERE IS STILL ONE MORE PURPOSE OF PUNISHMENT, HOWEVER, THAT FEW WOULD EVER ADMIT TO EVEN THEMSELVES...

RETALIATION.

RETALIATION IS NOT ABOUT BALANCE OR FAIRNESS.

WE'RE TALKING **VENGEANCE**, HERE. LITTLE MORE THAN THE EMOTIONAL DRIVE TO SIMPLY HURT THOSE WHO HAVE HURT US.

ALL THAT MATTERS IS
THAT YOU HURT SOMEONE,
YOU HURT SOCIETY,
AND SO SOCIETY IS GONNA
HURT YOU RIGHT BACK.

IT'S AN ANIMAL INSTINCT,
PROTECTIVE AND IMMEDIATE.

WE DON'T LIKE TO TALK ABOUT IT.
AND NOBODY EVER BRINGS IT
UP AS A FACTOR AT SENTENCING.

BUT IT WOULD BE
DISHONEST TO IGNORE IT.

AND THAT COMPLETES THIS SECTION ON THE PURPOSES OF *PUNISHMENT.*

THE STATE PUNISHES THOSE WHO COMMIT CRIMES — PARTLY IN THE HOPE OF PREVENTING FUTURE OFFENSES (VIA *REHABILITATION, DETERRENCE,* AND *REMOVAL*), AND PARTLY TO RESTORE A SENSE OF BALANCE AND FAIRNESS (VIA *RETRIBUTION*).

AND PARTLY BECAUSE SCREW YOU, THAT'S WHY (VIA *RETALIATION*).

NOW THAT WE'VE LAID THE GROUNDWORK OF WHAT *CRIME* AND *PUNISHMENT* ARE, IT'S TIME TO GET INTO THE NITTY-GRITTY OF THE *LAW.*

SO LET'S DIVE RIGHT INTO OUR NEXT PART, WHERE WE'LL TALK ABOUT *GUILT* AND *CULPABILITY.*

"I DIDN'T MEAN TO!"

AS WE'VE SEEN, OUR SENSE THAT PUNISHMENT MUST BE **DESERVED** IS VERY POWERFUL. PEOPLE SEEM TO HAVE AN INNATE SENSE OF **JUSTICE** THAT REQUIRES SOME PROPORTIONALITY BETWEEN THE OFFENSE AND THE RESULTING PENALTY.

THIS SENSE OF JUSTICE IS **POWERFUL.**

STUDIES HAVE SHOWN THAT EVEN **INFANTS** SHARE THIS DESIRE THAT WRONGDOERS BE PUNISHED, AND THAT PUNISHMENT BE DESERVED.

(PERHAPS FORTUNATELY FOR PARENTS, THERE'S NOT MUCH THEY CAN **DO** ABOUT IT.)

THIS DRIVE IS SO STRONG THAT, WHEN WE SEE BAD THINGS HAPPEN TO PERFECTLY **INNOCENT** PEOPLE, WE WANT TO THINK THAT THEY SOMEHOW HAD IT **COMING.**

PSYCHOLOGISTS CALL THIS THE "JUST WORLD" PHENOMENON, A COGNITIVE BIAS THAT EXPLAINS WHY SOMEONE MAY FEEL COMPELLED TO BLAME THE *VICTIM* OF A RAPE, OR MINIMIZE THE SUFFERING OF VICTIMS OF WAR ATROCITIES OR AIDS.

CLEARLY, THEY BROUGHT THIS ON THEMSELVES...

IT'S ALSO ONE OF THE REASONS WHY OUR EMOTIONS ARE SO MUCH STRONGER WHEN WE SEE VERY YOUNG CHILDREN SUFFERING...

UNLIKE ADULTS, THEY SIMPLY *COULDN'T* HAVE DONE ANYTHING TO *DESERVE* IT.

AS WE'LL SEE, THESE KINDS OF CONSIDERATIONS PLAY OUT IN CRIMINAL JUSTICE IN SEVERAL WAYS. OUR SENSE OF JUSTICE DEMANDS THAT THE STATE ONLY PUNISH PEOPLE WHO **DESERVE** IT.

BUT WHAT DOES THAT MEAN?

HOW DO WE KNOW WHAT SOMEONE DESERVES?

OR, TO PUT IT ANOTHER WAY, WHAT MAKES ONE PERSON MORE *CULPABLE* THAN ANOTHER?

THAT'S OBVIOUS! THE MORE HARMFUL THE ACT, THE MORE GUILTY THEY, UH...

HANG ON, "GUILTY" ISN'T THE SAME AS "CULPABLE" IS IT...

...OR IS IT?

HOW ABOUT WE LOOK AT SOME DIFFERENT SITUATIONS, AND SEE IF THAT HELPS.

FIRST, MEET JACK AND HIS DAUGHTER JILL.

JILL IS JUST STARTING TO EAT "GROWN UP" FOOD, AND JACK GIVES HER SOME ARTICHOKE TO TRY.

UNFORTUNATELY, NOBODY KNEW THAT JILL IS MORBIDLY ALLERGIC TO ARTICHOKES, AND SHE'S DEAD BEFORE THE AMBULANCE ARRIVES.

NOW MEET JAN AND HER BABY DEAN.

DEAN HAS HAD A NASTY COUGH ALL DAY, SO JAN GIVES HIM A DOSE OF HER EXTRA STRENGTH COUGH MEDICINE.

HE STOPS BREATHING AND IS DEAD IN MINUTES.

HERE'S CLYDE. HE'S AN EXTERMINATOR CALLED TO DEAL WITH A RAT PROBLEM AT A STORE NEXT TO THE LOCAL NURSERY SCHOOL.

HE KNOWS HE OUGHT TO BE MORE CAREFUL, WHAT WITH KIDS NEARBY, BUT HE'S IN A HURRY TO GET HOME TO WATCH THE GAME, AND HE JUST FLINGS PELLETS OF RAT POISON ALL OVER AND DRIVES OFF.

ONE OF THE PELLETS LANDS IN THE NURSERY SCHOOL PLAYGROUND, WHERE LITTLE BONNIE SHOVES IT IN HER MOUTH. SHE DIES, OF COURSE.

AND THIS IS ROMEO.

DEPRESSED OVER THE LOSS OF HIS JOB, HE PLANS TO COMMIT SUICIDE BY RUNNING A GAS GENERATOR IN HIS APARTMENT.

HE KNOWS THE FUMES WILL PROBABLY ASPHYXIATE HIS UPSTAIRS NEIGHBOR, WHOEVER THAT IS...

BUT HE JUST DOESN'T CARE.

AS IT HAPPENS, ROMEO SURVIVES. BUT HIS UPSTAIRS NEIGHBOR'S DAUGHTER JULIET DIES OF CARBON MONOXIDE POISONING IN HER CRIB.

FINALLY, MEET LUCY, A SINGLE MOTHER.

SHE'D RATHER JUST BE SINGLE.

SO SHE POISONS HER LITTLE BOY RICKY WITH PESTICIDE,

AND HE DIES.

FIVE CHILDREN.
EACH EQUALLY INNOCENT.
EACH EQUALLY DEAD.
EACH DEATH CLEARLY CAUSED
BY THE ACTIONS OF AN ADULT.

THE HARM IS THE **SAME** IN EACH CASE. AND YET MOST PEOPLE WOULD FEEL THAT **NONE** OF THE ADULTS ARE EQUALLY CULPABLE.

THE DIFFERENCE IS NOT IN THE HARM DONE, BUT IN THE **MENTAL STATE** OF THE PERSON WHO DID IT.

THIS MENTAL STATE, OR "**MENS REA**" IN LATIN, IS THE CRITICAL FACTOR IN CRIMINAL LAW.

IT IS WHAT MAKES THE DIFFERENCE BETWEEN A SERIOUS CRIME AND A MINOR CRIME — OR EVEN NO CRIME AT ALL.

"MENS REA" TRANSLATES LOOSELY AS "GUILTY MIND," OR PERHAPS "ACCUSED MIND."

SO WHAT ARE THESE DIFFERENT MENTAL STATES?

WHAT ARE WE LOOKING FOR WHEN WE DECIDE ONE PERSON DESERVES MORE PUNISHMENT THAN ANOTHER?

REMEMBER JACK AND JILL?

JACK KILLED HIS DAUGHTER BY **ACCIDENT.** MAYBE IT WAS A LITTLE ODD TO FEED HER ARTICHOKE, BUT NOBODY COULD HAVE IMAGINED THAT IT WOULD KILL HER.

OF ALL THESE CHILD KILLERS, JACK IS THE LEAST CULPABLE: NOT DESERVING ANY PUNISHMENT.

(THERE ARE SOME RARE OFFENSES WHERE EVEN ACCIDENTS ARE PUNISHED, BUT WE'LL GET TO THAT LATER.)

WHAT ABOUT JAN AND DEAN?

WELL, JAN DIDN'T EXPECT THAT GIVING HER BABY ADULT-STRENGTH COUGH MEDICINE WOULD BE FATAL. BUT YOU'D HAVE EXPECTED HER TO BE MORE CAREFUL. JAN WAS **NEGLIGENT.**

MOST OF THE TIME, NEGLIGENCE IS THE LEAST CULPABLE MENS REA THAT CAN BE PUNISHED — HERE PERHAPS AS A "NEGLIGENT HOMICIDE."

(THOUGH ONE MIGHT SAY SHE'S SUFFERED ENOUGH ALREADY.)

AND CLYDE?

HE KNEW THERE WERE LITTLE KIDS NEARBY, HE KNEW THAT HE WAS THROWING RAT POISON AROUND, SO HE KNEW THERE WAS A RISK THAT SOME LITTLE KID MIGHT EAT SOME.

BUT HE DID IT ANYWAY. HE ACTED *RECKLESSLY.*

THIS IS SOMEONE WHOM SOCIETY ALMOST CERTAINLY WANTS TO PUNISH, NOW.

HE'S PROBABLY FACING "MANSLAUGHTER" CHARGES, OR SOMETHING SIMILAR.

OKAY, SO WHAT ABOUT MISTER DEPRESSION OVER HERE? WHAT MAKES HIM ANY DIFFERENT FROM CLYDE?

ROMEO KNEW MORE THAN CLYDE DID. CLYDE MERELY KNEW THAT THERE WAS A RISK.

BUT ROMEO KNEW THAT IT ALMOST CERTAINLY WOULD HAPPEN.

HE WASN'T TRYING TO KILL JULIET ON PURPOSE, BUT HE KILLED HER *KNOWINGLY.*

AND FOR THAT, HE'S PROBABLY LOOKING AT SECOND-DEGREE MURDER CHARGES.

AND SO WE COME TO LUCY.

LUCY KILLED RICKY ON PURPOSE. IT'S WHAT SHE MEANT TO DO.

SHE KILLED HIM *INTENTIONALLY*.

WHEN SOMEONE COMMITS A CRIME INTENTIONALLY, SOCIETY DEMANDS THE MOST PUNISHMENT.

LUCY'S FACING MURDER ONE.

GOD, WHAT A DEPRESSING DISCUSSION. NO WONDER THAT BABY WAS SO ANGRY AT THE BEGINNING.

EVEN SO, NOW WE HAVE A
USEFUL SCALE OF CULPABILITY,
BASED ON THE MENTAL STATE
OF THE PERSON WHO DID IT.

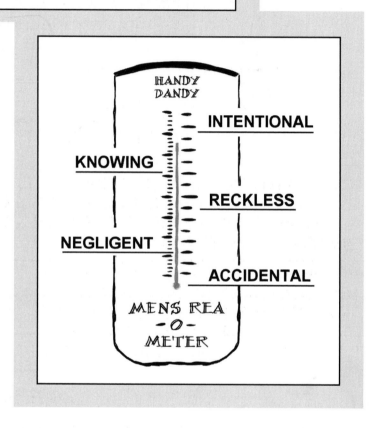

BUT THAT'S NOT ALL THERE IS TO IT.
NOT BY ANY STRETCH OF THE IMAGINATION...

"THE AXES OF EVIL"

IN CHAPTER 6, WE SAW THAT HOW **CULPABLE** SOMEONE IS DEPENDS ON THEIR **MENS REA**: THEIR MENTAL STATE WHEN THEY DID THE DEED.

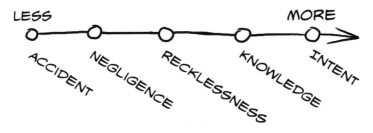

LESS ————————————————————— MORE →

ACCIDENT   NEGLIGENCE   RECKLESSNESS   KNOWLEDGE   INTENT

IT'S ALMOST AS IF, THE MORE THEY SHOULD HAVE KNOWN THE CONSEQUENCES OF THEIR ACTIONS, THE MORE CULPABLE THEY ARE, THE WORSE THE CRIME, AND THE HARSHER THE PUNISHMENT.

BUT WHAT IF, INSTEAD OF FOCUSING ON WHETHER SOMEONE **SHOULD** HAVE KNOWN THE CONSEQUENCES, WE ASK WHETHER THEY EVEN **COULD** HAVE KNOWN?

TAKE FOR EXAMPLE, A TODDLER WHO SWIPES SOME CANDY IN THE CHECKOUT LINE. THE KID ISN'T OLD ENOUGH TO KNOW IT'S WRONG. THE VERY CONCEPTS OF "PROPERTY" AND "NOT YOURS" ARE ENTIRELY FOREIGN, IMPOSSIBLE TO IMAGINE.

IT'S A PURELY INTENTIONAL THEFT, SO ON THE MENS REA SCALE THE KID IS AS CULPABLE AS CAN BE. AND YET FEW WOULD AGREE THAT THE TODDLER COMMITTED A CRIME.

IT'S NOT SO MUCH A QUESTION OF CULPABILITY AS IT IS OF **RESPONSIBILITY.**

SOCIETY DOESN'T WANT THE STATE TO PUNISH A CHILD WHO COULD NOT HAVE KNOWN WHAT SOCIETY'S RULES WERE IN THE FIRST PLACE.

THE PARENTS CAN DISCIPLINE THE KID ALL THEY WANT, HOWEVER (WITHIN REASON).

A CHILD IS NOT RESPONSIBLE (CRIMINALLY LIABLE) FOR ACTIONS HE COULDN'T HAVE KNOWN WERE WRONG.

THE SAME CAN BE TRUE OF ADULTS WHOSE CIRCUMSTANCES AFFECT THEIR ABILITY TO KNOW RIGHT FROM WRONG.

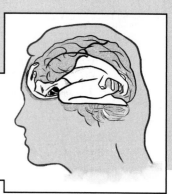

WE'LL GO OVER THIS IN MORE DETAIL WHEN WE START TALKING ABOUT DEFENSES.

OTHER THINGS AFFECT RESPONSIBILITY, TOO. CRIMINAL LIABILITY ALSO DEPENDS ON HOW DIRECTLY OR INDIRECTLY ONE'S ACTS CAUSED THE BAD RESULT.

WE'LL GO OVER THAT IN MORE DETAIL LATER AS WELL, BUT IN THE MEANTIME THINK OF THIS...

DONALD SHOOTS VICTOR, TRYING TO KILL HIM, BUT ONLY WOUNDS HIM.

AFTER VICTOR GETS TO THE HOSPITAL, IT COLLAPSES IN AN EARTHQUAKE, AND VICTOR DIES.

IT'S TRUE THAT, IF DONALD HADN'T SHOT HIM, VICTOR WOULDN'T HAVE BEEN IN THE HOSPITAL TO BE KILLED.

AND DONALD DID INTEND TO KILL HIM.

BUT HOW RESPONSIBLE IS DONALD FOR VICTOR'S DEATH?

TIME FOR...

Pin the Blame on Somebody

VERY RESPONSIBLE

KINDA RESPONSIBLE

SORTA RESPONSIBLE

NOT RESPONSIBLE

CAN I PLAY THIS ONE?

IT'S NOT A GAME, LADY JUSTICE.

ANYWAY, THE POINT IS THAT THE MORE **RESPONSIBLE** ONE IS FOR THE HARM DONE, THE MORE LIKELY ONE IS TO BE FOUND CRIMINALLY **LIABLE** FOR IT.

SO NOW WE HAVE A COUPLE OF FACTORS TO CONSIDER WHEN ASSESSING HOW **BAD** SOMEONE WAS:

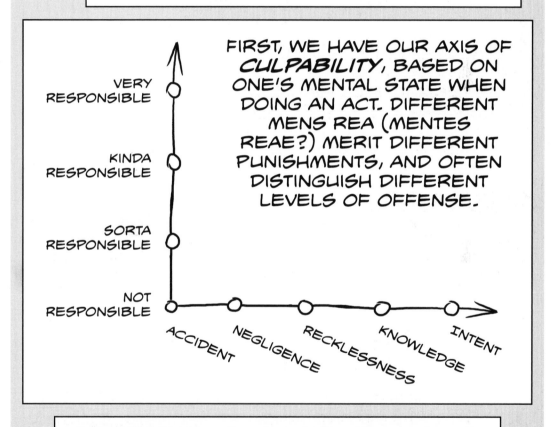

FIRST, WE HAVE OUR AXIS OF **CULPABILITY**, BASED ON ONE'S MENTAL STATE WHEN DOING AN ACT. DIFFERENT MENS REA (MENTES REAE?) MERIT DIFFERENT PUNISHMENTS, AND OFTEN DISTINGUISH DIFFERENT LEVELS OF OFFENSE.

ORTHOGONAL TO THAT ONE, WE HAVE THE AXIS OF **RESPONSIBILITY**, OR HOW LIABLE ONE IS FOR THE HARM DONE. THIS IS MORE INTUITIVE THAN FORMULAIC.

FOR A GIVEN HARM (SUCH AS A THEFT OF CANDY OR A KILLING) **WHERE** ONE FALLS ON THESE AXES GOES A LONG WAY TOWARD DETERMINING WHETHER AND HOW MUCH ONE SHOULD BE PUNISHED.

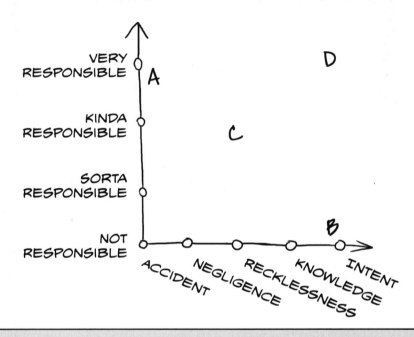

SO PEOPLE AT POINTS "A" AND "B," WHILE RESPONSIBLE FOR THE HARM ON THE ONE HAND, AND INTENDING IT ON THE OTHER, ARE NEVERTHELESS NOT LIKELY TO DESERVE PUNISHMENT.

SOMEONE AT POINT "C," HOWEVER, WAS BOTH RECKLESS AND KINDA RESPONSIBLE. THAT PERSON IS MUCH MORE LIKELY TO BE PUNISHED, AT LEAST A LITTLE BIT.

AND THE INTENTIONAL, VERY RESPONSIBLE GUY AT "D"? HE'S GOING DOWN.

BUT WAIT, THERE'S MORE!

IN ADDITION TO HOW BAD THE ACTOR'S MENTAL STATE WAS, AND HOW RESPONSIBLE FOR IT HE WAS, WE ALSO LOOK AT HOW BAD HE HIMSELF WAS.

SO ADD TO CULPABILITY AND RESPONSIBILITY THE AXIS OF *DEPRAVITY*.

CULPABILITY

RESPONSIBILITY

DEPRAVITY

NOW YOU'RE TALKING MY LANGUAGE!

TAKE TWO INTENTIONAL MURDERERS.

ONE, A HUSBAND ARGUING ABOUT HIS WIFE'S COOKING, KILLS HER WITH A SINGLE BLOW.

THE SECOND, A SADISTIC PSYCHOPATH, KILLS A YOUNG WOMAN...

HORRIFICALLY.

EACH ONE COMMITTED THE SAME CRIME, WITH THE SAME MENS REA, AND EACH IS EQUALLY RESPONSIBLE.

BUT LADY JUSTICE HERE WANTS THE STATE TO PUNISH THE SADISTIC KILLER FAR WORSE.

WHY?

BECAUSE HE WAS MORE
DEPRAVED, THAT'S WHY.

(AND LIKE RESPONSIBILITY, ASSESSING
DEPRAVITY IS MORE OF A GUT INSTINCT
THAN A REASONED DEDUCTION.)

SO THESE ARE OUR THREE "AXES OF EVIL"
THAT THE LAW USES TO FIGURE OUT
HOW BAD SOMEONE WAS.

CULPABILITY: LOGICAL.
HOW SEVERE THE OFFENSE IS;

RESPONSIBILITY: INTUITIVE.
HOW LIABLE (OR EXCUSED)
THE OFFENDER IS; AND

DEPRAVITY: INTUITIVE.
HOW BAD THE OFFENDER IS.

TAKEN TOGETHER, THESE DETERMINE
HOW DESERVING OF PUNISHMENT
SOMEONE IS FOR A GIVEN ACT.

BUT WHAT IS THIS "ACT" WE KEEP MENTIONING?

WE'LL GET TO THAT NEXT...

"WHAT HAVE YOU *DONE*?"

BEFORE THE STATE CAN PUNISH SOMEONE FOR HAVING COMMITTED A CRIME, IT FIRST HAS TO PROVE THAT THE CRIME WAS *COMMITTED*, AND THAT IT WAS COMMITTED BY THIS PARTICULAR PERSON.

AT TRIAL, IT IS USUALLY UP TO THE JURY TO DECIDE WHETHER THE GOVERNMENT ACTUALLY MANAGED TO *PROVE* ALL OF THAT.

FOR EXAMPLE, JOE HERE IS CHARGED WITH ASSAULT IN THE FIRST DEGREE, FOR PUTTING SIMON IN THE HOSPITAL FOR LIFE WITH SEVERE BRAIN DAMAGE.

HE DESERVED WORSE.

THEIR STATE HAS A SIMPLIFIED CRIMINAL CODE, WHICH DEFINES THE CRIME THIS WAY:

CRIM. CODE OF STATE X

A person commits Assault in the First Degree when he:

(1) Intends to kill, maim, or cause permanent and severe injury to another person; and

(2) Causes that person, or another person, to be maimed or permanently and severely injured.

AT TRIAL, THE PROSECUTOR IS GOING TO HAVE TO PROVE TWO THINGS: THE *"ELEMENTS"* OF THIS CRIME.

FIRST, THE MENS REA ELEMENT: THAT JOE *INTENDED* TO CAUSE THAT HARM TO SIMON.

OH, I INTENDED IT, ALL RIGHT.

BUT MERE INTENT IS NOT ENOUGH TO COMMIT THE CRIME. JOE NEEDS TO HAVE **DONE** SOMETHING AS WELL. THIS SECOND ELEMENT IS CALLED THE **ACTUS REUS.**

ACTUS REUS IS LATIN FOR "GUILTY ACT." IN OTHER WORDS, IT HAS TO BE MORE THAN JUST AN ACT. IT HAS TO BE A "GUILTY" ONE. BUT WHAT DOES THAT MEAN?

LET'S LOOK AT WHAT JOE DID.

JOE WANTED TO KILL SIMON. SO HE GOT A VOODOO DOLL FROM HIS LOCAL WITCH DOCTOR, AND STUCK SOME BIG PINS IN IT.

SURE ENOUGH, THE VERY NEXT DAY A BRICK FELL FROM A BUILDING AND PUT A DENT IN SIMON'S SKULL.

JOE HAD THE NECESSARY INTENT, AND HE CERTAINLY TOOK AN ACTION TO CARRY OUT THAT INTENT. BUT HIS ACT IS NOT A "GUILTY" ONE. *WHY?* BECAUSE HIS ACT DID NOT *CAUSE* THE HARM.

THAT'S A PRETTY OBVIOUS EXAMPLE. AND EQUALLY OBVIOUS IS THE CASE WHERE JOE *THREW* THE BRICK AT SIMON'S HEAD

APOLOGIES TO G. HERRIMAN

—ZETZ

POW

CAUSATION IS FAIRLY STRAIGHTFORWARD, MOST OF THE TIME.

BUT WHAT ABOUT SITUATIONS WHERE JOE SET IN MOTION A SERIES OF EVENTS THAT ULTIMATELY CAUSED THE INJURY?

NO MATTER HOW CONVOLUTED THE FACTS MAY BE, ALL YOU'RE LOOKING FOR IS WHETHER THE HARM WOULD HAVE HAPPENED ANYWAY, AND HOW CLOSELY RELATED THE ACT IS TO THE HARM.

OR *CAUSE IN FACT* AND *PROXIMATE CAUSE,* RESPECTIVELY.

IF SIMON WOULDN'T HAVE BEEN HURT "BUT FOR" JOE'S MAKING FACES AT THE PIGEON, THEN JOE'S ACT WAS A *CAUSE IN FACT* OF THE HARM.

BUT *PROXIMATE CAUSE* HAS TO DO WITH HOW LIKELY IT WAS THAT THE ACT WOULD HAVE CAUSED THAT HARM — HOW *PREDICTABLE* IT WAS.

THAT ONE IS MORE OF A GUT FEELING THAN A LOGICAL ANALYSIS.

IN THIS CASE, *NOBODY* COULD HAVE PREDICTED THAT SPOOKING THE PIGEON WOULD CAUSE SIMON TO GET STRUCK ON THE HEAD BY A BRICK. SO EVEN THOUGH JOE'S ACT WAS THE CAUSE IN FACT, IT WAS *NOT* THE PROXIMATE CAUSE, AND SO THERE IS *NO* ACTUS REUS.

JOE WILL BE GUILTY *ONLY* IF HE COMMITTED AN ACTUS REUS — AN ACT THAT CAUSED THE HARM PROHIBITED BY THAT LAW — WITH THE REQUIRED MENS REA.

THAT'S CALLED *"CONCURRENCE."*

SO IF JOE INTENDED TO HURT SIMON, BUT THEN ACCIDENTALLY HIT HIM WITH HIS CAR, *EVEN THOUGH* HE CAUSED THE HARM AND HAD THE RIGHT INTENT, HE DID NOT COMMIT THE ACT *WITH* THAT INTENT, AND SO HE IS NOT GUILTY.

OOPS!

NOW WHAT IF JOE MEANT TO MAIM SIMON, AND THREW A BRICK AT HIM, BUT MISSED AND MAIMED MAMIE INSTEAD?

HE MISSED AND MAIMED MAMIE INSTEAD!

THAT'S CALLED "*TRANSFERRED INTENT.*" JOE'S INTENT TO HURT SIMON GETS COUNTED TOWARD HIS HURTING MAMIE.

IN THIS CASE, THE STATUTE PLAINLY SAYS THAT IT'S STILL FIRST-DEGREE ASSAULT IF THE HARM HAPPENED TO A THIRD PERSON BUT EVEN IF IT HADN'T SAID SO, JOE IS STILL PROBABLY GOING TO BE GUILTY.

ALL IN ALL, ACTUS REUS IS PRETTY MUCH A MATTER OF COMMON SENSE. IT'S THE THING THE LAW SAYS "*DON'T DO.*"

EITHER YOU DID IT, OR YOU DIDN'T.

BUT WHAT IF YOU *ATTEMPTED* TO DO IT, WITH ALL THE MENS REA REQUIRED, BUT DIDN'T SUCCEED?

LET'S EXPLORE THAT NEXT...

CHAPTER 9.
ATTEMPT

"AT LEAST YOU TRIED"

YOU HAVEN'T EXACTLY BEEN MAKING A LOT OF FRIENDS AROUND HERE LATELY.

LET'S JUST SAY YOU SHOULD AVOID STANDING IN FRONT OF ANY WINDOWS. YOU NEVER KNOW WHO MIGHT BE LOOKING IN...

...JUST SAYIN'.

TAKE BILL HERE:

HE'D LIKE TO SEE YOU DEAD.

NOTHING WOULD GIVE HIM GREATER PLEASURE THAN TO LEARN YOU'VE SUFFERED SOME PAINFUL INJURY.

IN FACT, HE EVEN LIES AWAKE AT NIGHT PONDERING ALL THE WAYS HE COULD MAKE YOU SUFFER.

YOU SHOULD HEAR SOME OF THE NASTY SCHEMES HE'S PLOTTED AGAINST YOU...

...THEN AGAIN, MAYBE NOT.

DON'T WORRY, THOUGH.

FANTASIZING ABOUT YOUR SUFFERING IS THE MOST BILL HAS EVER DONE.

THAT'S MORE THAN CAN BE SAID FOR DANA, HOWEVER.

DANA THOROUGHLY **INTENDS** TO HURT YOU...

THE NEXT TIME YOU CROSS HER PATH, ANYWAY.

HONEY, THE ONLY REASON I'M NOT HUNTING YOU DOWN LIKE THE ANIMAL YOU ARE...

...IS YOU'RE JUST NOT WORTH THE EFFORT ANYMORE.

SO COUNT YOUR BLESSINGS — DANA'S GOT ALL THE INTENT IN THE WORLD, BUT SHE CAN'T BE BOTHERED **DOING** ANYTHING ABOUT IT AT THE MOMENT.

OH, YOU FORGOT ABOUT YOUR ESRTWHILE PARTNER?

YOU'D BETTER BELIEVE **HE** HASN'T FORGOTTEN.

...AND HE'S **LOOKING** FOR YOU.

FLINT'S INVESTING QUITE
A BIT OF SHOE LEATHER
(AND NOT AN INCONSIDERABLE
AMOUNT OF WHOOP-ASS)
TRACKING YOU DOWN OUT
THERE IN THE MEAN STREETS.

HE HASN'T FOUND YOU YET,

BUT BOY, WHEN HE *DOES*...

AND THEN THERE'S MAUDE.

SWEET LITTLE MAUDE.

YOU MADE QUITE AN IMPRESSION ON HER!

SO YOU COULDN'T HAVE BEEN ALL THAT SURPRISED WHEN SHE CAME BY TO TAKE A **POTSHOT** AT YOU LAST NIGHT.

DON'T KNOW HOW THE KID COULD HAVE **MISSED.** BUT SHE DID, AND NOW SHE THINKS YOU'RE SOME KIND OF RASPUTIN WHO CAN'T BE KILLED.

SHE'S **NEVER** GOING TO TRY TO HURT YOU AGAIN.

WHAT'S THE USE?

SO THAT'S FOUR PEOPLE WHO WANT YOU DEAD.

THE **QUESTION** IS, WHICH ONES COMMITTED A **CRIME** AGAINST YOU?

BILL DOESN'T INTEND TO KILL YOU, AND HASN'T DONE ANYTHING TO HURT YOU.

NO MENS REA,

NO ACTUS REUS?

NO CRIME.

MERELY WISHING HARM ON SOMEONE IS NOT SOMETHING THE STATE IS GOING TO PUNISH.

*CRIME IS SOMETHING YOU **DID**, NOT SOMETHING YOU **THOUGHT**.*

THE SAME GOES FOR DANA, WHO ACTUALLY **INTENDS** TO KILL YOU.

ALTHOUGH SHE'S LOADED WITH MENS REA, SHE HASN'T **DONE** ANYTHING WITH IT.

MENS REA WITHOUT SOME ACTUS REUS IS **NEVER** A CRIME.

SO DANA DOESN'T DESERVE TO BE PUNISHED, EITHER.

STILL, YOU PROBABLY OUGHT TO STEER CLEAR OF HER.

YOUR OLD PARTNER **FLINT MICHIGAN**, ON THE OTHER HAND, IS AN INTERESTING CASE.

FLINT HASN'T DONE ANYTHING TO YOU — HE HASN'T HURT YOU, HE HASN'T KILLED YOU. BUT IN **SOME** JURISDICTIONS HE'S ALREADY GUILTY OF THE CRIME OF **ATTEMPT.**

ATTEMPTED MURDER, TO BE PRECISE.

WHY??

FLINT HASN'T HURT YOU. HE HAS THE NECESSARY INTENT, BUT HE HASN'T COMMITTED THE ACTUS REUS FOR ASSAULT OR MURDER.

WHY SHOULD HE BE PUNISHED FOR SOMETHING HE HASN'T EVEN **DONE** YET?

WELL, LET'S LOOK AT THE
PURPOSES OF PUNISHMENT AGAIN:

REHABILITATION?
FLINT'S TRYING TO COMMIT A CRIME, HE'S GONE
BEYOND MERE PLANNING, AND HAS TAKEN STEPS
TO CARRY OUT THE CRIME? SOUNDS *DANGEROUS.*
MAYBE HE NEEDS *CORRECTION.*

DETERRENCE?
WE DON'T WANT PEOPLE ACTIVELY TRYING TO COMMIT
CRIMES — WHAT IF THEY SUCCEED? AND WE CERTAINLY
DON'T WANT FLINT TO TRY TO KILL YOU *AGAIN.*

REMOVAL?
DUDE, FLINT IS *DANGEROUS.* HE NEEDS TO BE
LOCKED AWAY. THE MERE FACT THAT HE HASN'T
SUCCEEDED IN KILLING YOU *YET* DOESN'T HAVE
ANYTHING TO DO WITH IT.

RETRIBUTION AND RETALIATION?
THESE DON'T REALLY APPLY.
FLINT HASN'T DONE ANY *HARM* YET, SO THERE'S
NOTHING TO REACT TO.

NO HARM,
NO FOUL?

AND THIS IS WHERE WE SEE HOW BIG A
ROLE *RETRIBUTION* PLAYS AS A PURPOSE
OF PUNISHMENT. BECAUSE ALTHOUGH
ATTEMPTED CRIMES DO GET PUNISHED,
THEY DON'T GET PUNISHED AS *SEVERELY*
AS COMPLETED ONES.

IN PRINCIPLE, THERE'S NO DIFFERENCE BETWEEN SOMEONE WHO ATTEMPTS A MURDER AND SOMEONE WHO SUCCEEDS IN KILLING. BOTH ARE *EQUALLY* BAD, POSE THE *SAME* DANGERS, AND HAVE THE *SAME* CRIMINAL INTENT. THE ONLY DIFFERENCE IS WHEN THEY GOT CAUGHT — A MATTER OF *PURE LUCK* THAT HAS NOTHING TO DO WITH THEIR "BADNESS."

BUT THERE IS A DIFFERENCE IN *PUNISHMENT* (IN MOST JURISDICTIONS). AND THE ONLY REASON IS THAT THERE'S NOTHING TO *AVENGE.*

SO FLINT'S OUT THERE, POUNDING THE PAVEMENT LOOKING FOR YOU, WITH THE INTENT TO KILL YOU WHEN HE FINDS YOU. AGAIN, IN SOME JURISDICTIONS THAT'S ENOUGH TO CHARGE HIM WITH ATTEMPT.

OTHER JURISDICTIONS ARE GOING TO REQUIRE A BIT MORE, HOWEVER. MAYBE GOING TO YOUR HOME WITH A GUN, OR PERHAPS ACTUALLY TAKING AIM, BEFORE BEING ARRESTED.

AND STILL OTHERS ARE GOING TO WAIT UNTIL HE'S STARTED *SHOOTING* BEFORE THEY'LL CALL IT A CRIMINAL ATTEMPT.

BETWEEN THE THOUGHT AND THE DEED, THERE IS A WHOLE CONTINUUM OF INTERMEDIATE STEPS.

AT SOME POINT, THEY CROSS THE LINE FROM MERE "PREPARATION," WHICH IS *NOT* A CRIME, TO "ATTEMPT," WHICH *IS*.

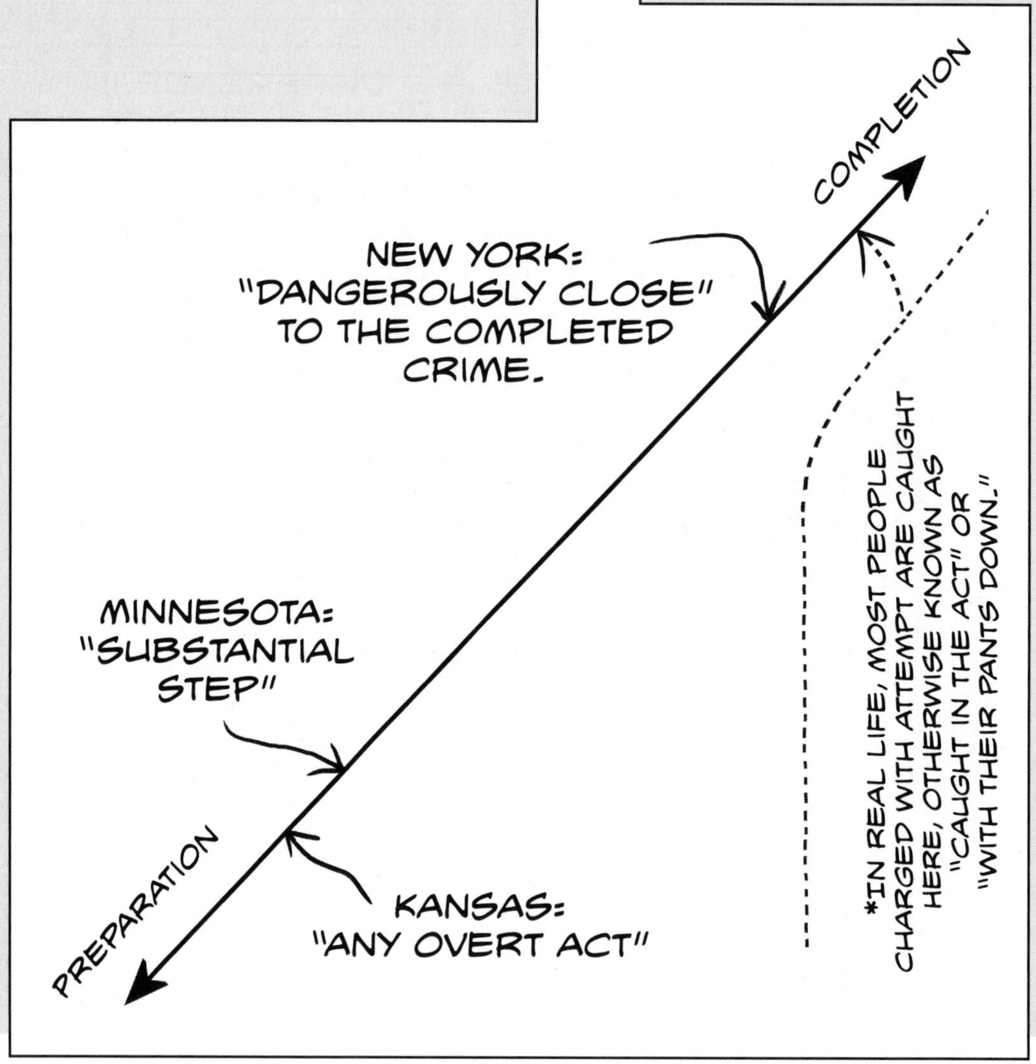

COMPLETION

NEW YORK: "DANGEROUSLY CLOSE" TO THE COMPLETED CRIME.

MINNESOTA: "SUBSTANTIAL STEP"

PREPARATION

KANSAS: "ANY OVERT ACT"

*IN REAL LIFE, MOST PEOPLE CHARGED WITH ATTEMPT ARE CAUGHT HERE, OTHERWISE KNOWN AS "CAUGHT IN THE ACT" OR "WITH THEIR PANTS DOWN."

ALTHOUGH THERE ARE MANY WAYS THE LINE GETS DRAWN, IT'S USEFUL TO LUMP THEM ALL INTO TWO UNDERLYING POLICIES:

JURISDICTIONS THAT DRAW THE LINE CLOSER TO THE INITIAL *IDEA* HAVE A MORE *SUBJECTIVE* CONCERN ABOUT FLINT'S MINDSET — IF HE'S FIRMLY DECIDED TO COMMIT THE CRIME, THEN HE DESERVES TO BE PUNISHED, THEY'D SAY.

JURISDICTIONS THAT DRAW THE LINE CLOSER TO THE COMPLETED *ACT* HAVE A MORE *OBJECTIVE* CONCERN ABOUT FLINT'S ACTIONS — ONLY PUNISHING HIM IF WHAT HE ACTUALLY DID WAS DANGEROUS.

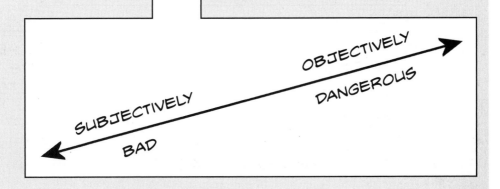

NOTE THAT THE CONTINUUM IS ONLY MEASURING THE ACTUS REUS. THAT'S BECAUSE FOR **ALL** ATTEMPTS, THE NECESSARY MENS REA IS THE SAME:

INTENT.

THAT'S PRETTY OBVIOUS, IF YOU THINK ABOUT IT.

"ATTEMPT" SORT OF MEANS "TRYING," DOESN'T IT?

AND IF IT'S NOT **INTENTIONAL,**

YOU'RE NOT **TRYING!**

NOW THE CLOSER THE LINE IS DRAWN TO THE "IDEA" END OF THE SPECTRUM, THE MORE LIKELY IT IS TO CAUSE SOME UNFAIR RESULTS.

PROBABLY   ??   PROBABLY NOT

IDEA   ACT

YOU'RE GOING TO WIND UP PENALIZING PEOPLE WHO, FOR WHATEVER REASON, WOULDN'T HAVE ACTUALLY COMMITTED THE OFFENSE IN THE END.

THE GREATER THE DISTANCE FROM THE CRIME, THE LESS SURE WE ARE THAT THE CRIME WAS EVER REALLY GOING TO *HAPPEN.*

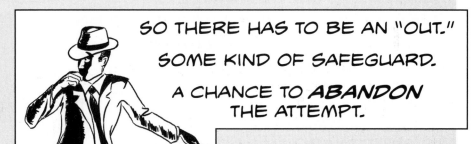

SO THERE HAS TO BE AN "OUT."

SOME KIND OF SAFEGUARD.

A CHANCE TO *ABANDON* THE ATTEMPT.

YOU WANT TO GIVE PEOPLE A CHANCE — AN INCENTIVE, EVEN — TO DECIDE *NOT* TO DO THE HARM.

THE CLOSER THE LINE IS DRAWN TO THE MERE FORMULATION OF THE IDEA, THEREFORE, THE MORE LIKELY THE JURISDICTION IS GOING TO HAVE A DEFENSE OF *ABANDONMENT.*

SO WITH THAT IN MIND, LET'S LOOK AT MAUDE.

SHE **USED** TO WANT TO KILL YOU, BUT NOW SHE'S COMPLETELY **GIVEN UP** THE IDEA. SHE NO LONGER INTENDS TO CAUSE YOU ANY HARM, AND ISN'T A DANGER TO ANYONE ANYMORE.

DOES MAUDE HAVE AN ABANDONMENT DEFENSE?

HECK, NO.

MAUDE CHANGED HER MIND, BUT ONLY AFTER SHE'D GONE WAY OVER TOWARD THE "COMPLETED" END OF THE SPECTRUM.

BLAM

THE REASON SHE DIDN'T COMPLETE YOUR MURDER IS NOT THAT SHE CHANGED HER MIND BEFORE SHOOTING AT YOU — IT'S THAT SHE **MISSED**.

TIMING IS EVERYTHING.

TO HAVE A VALID ABANDONMENT DEFENSE, MAUDE NEEDED TO STOP HAVING ANY INTENT TO COMMIT THE CRIME, **AND** IT NEEDED TO HAVE BEEN OF HER OWN FREE WILL.

IT **DOESN'T** COUNT IF SHE CHANGED HER MIND BECAUSE SHE WAS AFRAID SHE'D GET CAUGHT,

OR BECAUSE SHE COULDN'T SHOOT STRAIGHT,

OR BECAUSE SHE FIGURED SHE'D WAIT UNTIL A BETTER OPPORTUNITY CAME ALONG.

ABANDONMENT MEANS A **COMPLETE CHANGE OF HEART.**

AND AGAIN, IT'S NOT A DEFENSE IN PLACES WHERE THE ATTEMPT LINE IS DRAWN CLOSER TO THE COMPLETED ACT.

BY THAT POINT, WHAT'S BEEN DONE IS SERIOUS ENOUGH THAT SOCIETY WON'T CONDONE IT, EVEN IF THE PERSON CHANGES HER MIND LATER.

ONE OTHER THING:

REMEMBER JOE?

HE TRIED TO KILL SIMON BY STICKING PINS IN A VOODOO DOLL. IS HE GUILTY OF ATTEMPT?

COME BACK SOON, Y' HEAR?

HE HAD THE RIGHT MENS REA, AND HE CERTAINLY TOOK STEPS TO CARRY OUT HIS INTENT.

BUT THERE IS NO WAY HIS ACTION COULD CONCEIVABLY WORK.

IT'S IMPOSSIBLE.

SO NO, HE'S NOT GUILTY OF ATTEMPT.

HE HAS THE DEFENSE OF *IMPOSSIBILITY*.

BUT FRICK AND FRACK, ON THE OTHER HAND, DO NOT HAVE THAT DEFENSE.

FRICK PLANTED A BOMB IN YOUR MAILBOX.

(WHAT *IS* IT WITH YOU, ANYWAY?)

THE BOMB'S FUSE WAS DEFECTIVE, HOWEVER, SO IT COULDN'T GO BOOM.

HE'S TRYING TO COMMIT THE CRIME, BUT IT'S *IMPOSSIBLE.* UNLIKE JOE, HOWEVER, HE COULD HAVE SUCCEEDED BUT FOR CIRCUMSTANCES BEYOND HIS CONTROL, OR OF WHICH HE WAS UNAWARE.

FRICK IS STILL DANGEROUS, AND SO HE'S STILL GUILTY.

AND FRACK OVER HERE IS A DRUG DEALER. HE BOUGHT A TRUCKLOAD OF KILOS FROM A NEW SUPPLIER WHO TURNED OUT TO BE A COP.

ACTUALLY, HE BOUGHT A TRUCKLOAD OF TALCUM POWDER INSTEAD OF COCAINE.

THOUGH IT WAS IMPOSSIBLE FOR HIM TO HAVE BOUGHT COCAINE IN THIS SITUATION — IT WAS ONLY EVER GOING TO BE TALC — FRACK IS *STILL* GOING TO BE GUILTY OF ATTEMPTED POSSESSION OF COCAINE.

WHAT HE WAS TRYING TO DO WAS ILLEGAL, AND ONLY IMPOSSIBLE DUE TO HIS OWN MISTAKE AS TO THE *FACTS* OF THE SITUATION. HE'S STILL "DANGEROUS," AND SO HE'S STILL GUILTY OF ATTEMPT.

AND THAT'S IT FOR THE CONCEPT OF *ATTEMPT.*

ATTEMPT MUST BE INTENTIONAL, IT CAN'T BE INHERENTLY IMPOSSIBLE, AND DIFFERENT JURISDICTIONS DRAW THE LINE IN DIFFERENT PLACES (BUT THOSE THAT DRAW THE LINE SOONER ALSO PROVIDE THE CHANCE TO ABANDON THE ATTEMPT).

NOW GO THANK YOUR LUCKY STARS THAT YOU'RE STILL BREATHING, AND LET'S START TALKING ABOUT ACCOMPLICES AND CONSPIRACIES...

"WE'LL ALL GO DOWN TOGETHER"

IT ALL STARTED WITH A SUMMONS FROM THE BIG CHEESE.

HE WANTED ME TO COMMIT THE PERFECT HEIST — A BROAD DAYLIGHT ROBBERY OF THE FAMOUS MAGUFFIN LOCKED IN THE BIG BANK'S TIGHTEST VAULT.

I'D PICK MY OWN TEAM, HE'D FINANCE IT, AND WE'D SPLIT THE PROFITS 60/40.

AS USUAL.

SO I ROUNDED UP MY TEAM:

NICK LEDWAY — GETAWAY DRIVER EXTRAORDINAIRE.

The Wheels

DOCTOR SYNTHCORE — BEST SCHEMER IN THE BIZ.

The Brains

WHAT, YOU THINK ALL THAT IRANIAN NUKE MONEY JUST LAUNDERED ITSELF?

MRS. FLAVORS — HACKER, JACKER, SAFECRACKER.

JUST GOT OUT OF THE PEN...

The Expert

...STILL HAS TEN YEARS LEFT ON HER SENTENCE.

JUDGE BAHR, THE HEAVY.

IF THERE'S PERSUADING TO BE DONE...

The Heavy

...THERE'S NOBODY MORE PERSUASIVE.

AND SO WE BEGAN.

DR. SYNTHCORE CAME UP WITH A DEVIOUS PLAN, ONE THAT WAS ALMOST CERTAIN TO SUCCEED.

BUT I NEED MORE DATA!

WITHOUT TELLING ANYONE ELSE, HE HIRED BOB CHASE TO CASE THE BANK.

I NEED TO KNOW WHEN THIS GUARD LEAVES HIS POST.

CHASE SAW HOW THE BANK GUARD LEFT HIS POST TO FLIRT WITH ONE OF THE TELLERS.

FRANK, YOU BUG ME LIKE THIS EVERY DAY.

YOU GONNA REPORT ME?

NAH, IT'S KINDA SWEET.

MEANWHILE, DR. SYNTHCORE PICKED UP ALL THE FANCY EQUIPMENT WE NEEDED FROM DRAKE, WHO RUNS THE LOCAL SPY GADGET STORE.

THE NEXT DAY, DR. SYNTHCORE TOLD ME THE PLAN...

AND HE WAS *FINISHED*. I MADE SURE HE NEVER MET ANYONE ELSE ON THE TEAM EXCEPT FOR ME.

I BRIEFED THE OTHERS MYSELF, LATER.

THE JOB

AS LEDWAY IDLED OUT FRONT IN THE GETAWAY CAR...

...MRS. FLAVORS AND I, POSING AS HUSBAND AND WIFE, WENT INSIDE TO ASK ABOUT A LOAN.

WHILE WE SPOKE TO THE LOAN OFFICER, BAHR GOT IN THE LONGEST LINE AND KEPT AN EYE ON THE WHOLE SCENE.

RIGHT ON SCHEDULE, THE SECURITY GUARD FLIRTED WITH THE TELLER

BAHR NODDED TO MRS. FLAVORS

AND SHE EXCUSED HERSELF TO GO TO THE LADIES' ROOM.

SHE HAD FIVE MINUTES.

DR. SYNTHCORE HAD FIGURED THAT THE VAULT WAS LOCKED ELECTRONICALLY, AND HAD LIGHTS AND ALL KINDS OF ELECTRIC GIZMOS INSIDE, AND ALL THAT STUFF NEEDED WIRING...

...SO MRS. FLAVORS WENT IN WITH THE WIRES.

SPEAKING OF DR. SYNTHCORE, WHILE ALL OF THIS WAS GOING ON AT THE BANK, HE WAS ACROSS TOWN MEETING WITH A SUIT WHO WANTED HIM TO HELP PLAN A MULTINATIONAL COMPUTER FRAUD.

SYNTHCORE AGREED, AND WAS STARTING TO GET THE DETAILS, WHEN THE SUIT SUDDENLY SHOWED HIM A BADGE AND ARRESTED HIM FOR CONSPIRACY TO COMMIT WIRE FRAUD.

BACK AT THE BANK, THERE WAS TROUBLE...

BAHR SAW THE MANAGER INTERRUPT THE GUARD AND SEND HIM BACK TO HIS POST.

BAHR PANICKED, REACHING FOR A GUN TO DISTRACT THE GUARD AND SOMEHOW STALL FOR TIME.

BYSTANDER HOLDEN SUDDENLY FIGURED OUT EVERYTHING THAT WAS GOING ON, BUT DID NOTHING TO STOP IT.

I HOPE THEY ROB THEM BLIND!

BAHR PULLED HIS GUN, THE SECURITY GUARD SHOT AT BAHR, MISSED, AND KILLED A BABY IN A STROLLER OUTSIDE ON THE SIDEWALK.

MRS. FLAVORS HEARD THE SHOOTING AND SCREAMING, BUT PATIENTLY FINISHED CRACKING INTO THE BOX AND ESCAPED WITH THE MAGUFFIN.

BAHR DASHED INTO THE GETAWAY CAR...

...AND HE AND LEDWAY SPED OFF WITHOUT US.

MRS. FLAVORS REJOINED ME IN THE CONFUSION, AND WE STROLLED OUT OF THE BANK UNNOTICED.

IT'S BEAUTIFUL!

WE HAD THE MAGUFFIN.

BUT THINGS WERE TURNING INTO A TERRIBLE MESS...

THE MESS

LEDWAY DECIDED TO DITCH HIS CAR, FEARING IT HAD BEEN NOTICED. IT WASN'T PART OF THE PLAN, BUT HE SWAPPED CARS WITH HIS BUDDY DAN.

DAN **KNEW** WHAT LEDWAY WAS UP TO, AND HE GLADLY HELPED HIM OUT.

EVEN SO, LEDWAY AND BAHR WERE THE FIRST ONES TO ARRIVE AT THE RENDEZVOUS.

big cheese

LEDWAY DROPPED BAHR OFF AND SKEDADDLED, AFRAID OF BEING CAUGHT. NOBODY'S SEEN HIM SINCE.

I ARRIVED NEXT, WITHOUT MRS. FLAVORS. WE'D GOTTEN SEPARATED EN ROUTE. SHE SHOWED UP 15 MINUTES LATER WITH A WAD OF CASH.

SEEMS SHE'D STOPPED ON THE WAY TO HACK AN ATM. NOT PART OF THE PLAN, JUST FOR THE FUN OF IT.

I ASKED HER TO LET ME HAVE THE MAGUFFIN, AND FOOLISHLY LET IT SLIP THAT I'D BE GIVING IT TO THE BIG CHEESE.

SHE DECIDED TO KEEP IT, AND SELL IT TO HIM HERSELF.

BAHR DREW HIS GUN ON HER, I YELLED AT THEM TO STOP IT, WE COULD WORK SOMETHING OUT...

...AND A PACK OF FEDERAL AGENTS BUSTED IN, WITH SYNTHCORE AND THE BIG CHEESE IN TOW.

AND THAT WAS PRETTY MUCH THE END OF THAT.

SO NOW THE QUESTION IS:

WHO CAN BE CHARGED WITH WHAT?

FIRST, WE'VE GOT **SOLICITATION.**

WHEN THE BIG CHEESE ASKED ME TO DO THE HEIST, HE COMMITTED THE CRIME OF SOLICITATION.

EVEN IF I'D SAID NO, THE BIG CHEESE WOULD STILL HAVE BEEN GUILTY.

THE CRIME OF SOLICITATION OCCURS WHEN YOU TRY TO GET SOMEONE ELSE TO COMMIT A CRIME.

JUST AS WITH ATTEMPT, YOU'RE **TRYING**, SO THE MENS REA IS **INTENT**. (AND THE ULTIMATE CRIME NEVER NEEDS TO BE COMPLETED.)

SOME JURISDICTIONS PUNISH SOLICITATION AS A MINOR OFFENSE ONLY, OTHERS WITH A LESSER PROPORTION OF WHAT THE INTENDED CRIME WOULD HAVE GOTTEN. FEW PUNISH IT AS SEVERELY AS THE INTENDED CRIME ITSELF, HOWEVER.

(I ALSO SOLICITED LEDWAY, SYNTHCORE, FLAVORS, AND BAHR WHEN I HIRED THEM ON.)

NEXT WE HAVE THE **THEFT** OF THE MAGUFFIN FROM THE BIG BANK.

MRS. FLAVORS IS THE ONLY ONE WHO PHYSICALLY BROKE IN AND STOLE IT, BUT SHE IS NOT THE ONLY ONE WHO IS GOING TO BE LIABLE FOR THAT CRIME.

SHE HAD SEVERAL ACCOMPLICES.

SO NOW LET'S TALK ABOUT
ACCOMPLICE LIABILITY.

UNLIKE SOLICITATION AND ATTEMPT (AND CONSPIRACY, AS WE'LL SOON SEE), BEING AN ACCOMPLICE IS **NOT** A SEPARATE CRIME. IT'S WHAT MAKES MULTIPLE PEOPLE LIABLE FOR THE SAME CRIME.

ALL THAT'S NEEDED TO BE AN ACCOMPLICE TO A CRIME IS TO **HELP** IT HAPPEN, WITH THE NECESSARY **MENS REA** FOR THAT OFFENSE.

THERE ARE **LOTS** OF WAYS TO HELP A CRIME — PLANNING IT, BEING A LOOKOUT, DRIVING A GETAWAY CAR ARE JUST A FEW.

ALL FOUR OF THESE PLAYERS, AS WELL AS THE CHEESE AND I, ARE ACCESSORIES TO THE BIG HEIST, AND ALL ARE EQUALLY **GUILTY** OF THE THEFT.

CHASE AND DAN, LIKEWISE, ARE ALSO ACCOMPLICES TO THE CRIME, EVEN THOUGH NEITHER WAS PART OF THE ORIGINAL SCHEME.

CHASE HELPED THE DOCTOR **PLAN** THE HEIST. HE DID SO INTENTIONALLY. SO HE'S JUST AS GUILTY OF THE THEFT AS THE REST OF US.

AND DAN HELPED LEDWAY AND BAHR *ESCAPE.* HE HELPED AFTER THE CRIME WAS OVER, SO IN SOME PLACES HE'D BE CHARGED WITH THE SEPARATE CRIME OF "ACCESSORY AFTER THE FACT," BUT THE LOGIC IS THE SAME EITHER WAY.

BUT NOT EVERYONE WHO HELPS A CRIME TAKE PLACE IS AN ACCOMPLICE.

DRAKE, FOR EXAMPLE, IS NOT AN ACCOMPLICE. YES, HE SOLD DR. S. THE EQUIPMENT WE NEEDED, BUT HE **DIDN'T** DO SO WITH ANY CRIMINAL MENS REA.

AND HOLDEN COULD HAVE STOPPED THE CRIME, BUT CHOSE NOT TO.

HE EVEN HOPED THE CRIME SUCCEEDED. BUT THAT'S NOT ENOUGH FOR ACCOMPLICE LIABILITY.

I HOPE THEY ROB THEM BLIND!

GENERALLY SPEAKING, YOU'RE NOT GOING TO BE LIABLE FOR *FAILING* TO ACT, OR FOR SELLING EQUIPMENT TO A CRIMINAL. YOU DON'T HAVE A DUTY TO POLICE OTHERS.

NOW BACK TO CHASE FOR A MOMENT. LET'S SAY HE DIDN'T HAVE THE NECESSARY INTENT TO CARRY OUT THE THEFT. MAYBE HE DIDN'T CARE ONE WAY OR THE OTHER.

BUT HE STILL THOUGHT IT WAS *LIKELY* THAT DR. S. WAS PLANNING A CRIME. SHOULD CHASE BE LET OFF THE HOOK, JUST BECAUSE HE DIDN'T HAVE THE NECESSARY MENS REA TO BE AN ACCOMPLICE?

SOME COURTS ARE GOING TO SAY HE INTENDED TO AID IN THE COMMISSION, AND SIMPLY APPLY THAT INTENT TO GIVE HIM ACCOMPLICE LIABILITY. A STRAIGHTFORWARD APPROACH USED BY SOME OTHER STATES, HOWEVER, IS TO MAKE SUCH INDIFFERENT ASSISTANCE A CRIME ITSELF.

SO PLACES LIKE NEW YORK HAVE THE CRIME OF "CRIMINAL *FACILITATION*," A MISDEMEANOR, WHEN YOU BELIEVE YOU'RE HELPING SOMEONE COMMIT A FELONY AND ACTUALLY DO HELP OUT.

AGAIN, HOWEVER, BEING AN ACCOMPLICE IS NOT A SEPARATE CRIME. INSTEAD, IT'S WHAT MAKES YOU LIABLE FOR THE CRIME YOU HELPED COMMIT.

BUT ACCOMPLICE LIABILITY ISN'T THE ONLY WAY TO CHARGE MULTIPLE PEOPLE WITH THE SAME CRIME. MOST JURISDICTIONS (BUT NOT ALL) HAVE A SEPARATE CRIME THAT LETS THE STATE PROSECUTE PEOPLE FOR **AGREEING** TO COMMIT A CRIME.

SO NOW LET'S TALK ABOUT...

CONSPIRACY

LIKE ATTEMPT AND SOLICITATION, CONSPIRACY IS WHAT'S CALLED AN "INCHOATE" CRIME.

IN OTHER WORDS, WHETHER THE INTENDED OFFENSE EVER HAPPENS IS UNIMPORTANT.

THE MERE CIRCUMSTANCES ALONE ARE PUNISHABLE ENOUGH.

WITH CONSPIRACY, WHAT'S CRIMINAL IS NOT ANY PARTICULAR ACT, BUT THE MERE AGREEMENT BETWEEN PEOPLE TO COMMIT A CRIME.

IN OTHER WORDS, **AGREEING** TO COMMIT A CRIME IS ITSELF DEEMED DANGEROUS ENOUGH TO SOCIETY TO BE PUNISHABLE.

SO WE'RE AGREED: NEXT MONDAY, WE GO TO THE DUKE'S PALACE...

SOME LAWS REQUIRE NOTHING MORE THAN THE MERE AGREEMENT. THAT WAS THE COMMON-LAW DEFINITION OF THE CRIME.

BUT TODAY, MOST LAWS REQUIRE SOMETHING MORE — THAT AT LEAST ONE OF THE CONSPIRATORS COMMITTED AN *"OVERT ACT"* IN FURTHERANCE OF THE CONSPIRACY.

PEOPLE USUALLY SAY "CO-CONSPIRATORS" INSTEAD OF JUST "CONSPIRATORS." BUT THE "CO" ALWAYS STRIKES ME AS REDUNDANT.

IN OUR CASE, A LOT OF US CAN BE CHARGED WITH CONSPIRACY.

EACH OF US IN THIS CHART AGREED AND INTENDED THAT THE MAGUFFIN GET STOLEN.

IT DOESN'T MATTER THAT LEDWAY, FLAVORS, AND BAHR NEVER KNEW SYNTHCORE, OR THAT CHASE EVEN EXISTED. IT DOESN'T MATTER WHETHER THEIR ROLE WAS BIG OR TINY. IT DOESN'T MATTER WHETHER THEY JOINED THE CONSPIRACY AT THE OUTSET OR LATER ON.

ALL THAT MATTERS IS THE ACTUS REUS OF **AGREEING** TO GET THAT CRIME COMMITTED, WITH WHATEVER MENS REA THAT OBJECT CRIME WOULD HAVE REQUIRED.

AN AGREEMENT, BY THE WAY, DOESN'T HAVE TO BE AN EXPLICIT CONTRACT OR EVEN AN ORAL COMMUNICATION. THE AGREEMENT CAN BE *TACIT*, PROVED MERELY BY ONE'S ACTIONS.

BUT WHAT **REALLY** SETS CONSPIRACY APART FROM ALL OTHER CRIMES IS THAT NOW THE STATE DOESN'T HAVE TO PROVE THE THEFT ITSELF — ALL IT HAS TO PROVE IS THE CONSPIRACY, AND IT GETS TO PUNISH US!

WELL, THAT SURE MAKES MY JOB A LOT EASIER!

ALSO, SOME JURISDICTIONS (BUT BY NO MEANS ALL) WILL SAY THAT EACH OF US IS GUILTY OF EVERY CRIME COMMITTED BY **EVERY OTHER** CONSPIRATOR, SO LONG AS IT WAS COMMITTED IN FURTHERANCE OF THE CONSPIRACY.

SO WHEN BAHR BROUGHT A GUN TO THE BANK AND STARTED WAVING IT AROUND, **ALL** OF US WOULD BE GUILTY OF THAT CRIME, TOO, IN ADDITION TO THE THEFT OF THE MAGUFFIN.

SIMILARLY, IF LEDWAY HAD STOLEN HIS SECOND GETAWAY CAR (INSTEAD OF TRADING WITH DAN), THEN ALL OF US CONSPIRATORS WOULD BE LIABLE AS ACCOMPLICES IN THE THEFT OF THE CAR.

WE'D BE LIABLE UNDER THAT RULE EVEN THOUGH WE HAD **NO IDEA** THAT LEDWAY WAS GOING TO DO IT.

WE CONSPIRED TO COMMIT CRIME "A". NOW, WHEN CRIME "B" HAPPENS AS A DIRECT RESULT, IT IS GOING TO BE ATTRIBUTED TO ALL OF US.

NO WONDER CONSPIRACY IS OFTEN CALLED "THE PROSECUTOR'S FAVORITE WEAPON."

THEY CAN CHARGE YOU EVEN THOUGH THEY CAN'T PROVE THE "REAL" CRIME, AND THEY CAN CHARGE EVERYONE WITH EVERYONE ELSE'S ACTS.

WOULD MRS. FLAVORS'S THEFT FROM THE ATM BE ATTRIBUTED TO THE REST OF US CONSPIRATORS?

NO, BECAUSE IT WAS NOT DONE IN FURTHERANCE OF THE CONSPIRACY. IT WAS A SEPARATE CRIME, ON HER OWN, AND HAD NOTHING TO DO WITH THE HEIST.

IS IT POSSIBLE TO GET OUT OF A CONSPIRACY WITHOUT GETTING IN TROUBLE? IS IT LIKE AN ATTEMPT THAT'S DEFINED CLOSER TO THE IDEA THAN THE OFFENSE, OR IS IT A COMPLETED OFFENSE FROM THE MOMENT OF AN AGREEMENT?

YEAH, WHAT IF I HAD WITHDRAWN FROM THE CONSPIRACY BEFORE THE HEIST TOOK PLACE?

YOU SHOULD KNOW BETTER THAN THAT, JUDGE. ONCE YOU'D AGREED TO TAKE PART, THE CRIME OF CONSPIRACY WAS COMPLETE THE MOMENT CHASE STARTED CASING THE BANK.

HOWEVER, YOU WOULDN'T HAVE BEEN LIABLE FOR ANY SUBSTANTIVE CRIMES COMMITTED BY THE CONSPIRATORS AFTER YOUR WITHDRAWAL.

IN SOME STATES, YOU'D HAVE A DEFENSE IF YOU VOLUNTARILY RENOUNCED YOUR CRIMINAL PURPOSE AND CALLED THE COPS ON YOUR EX-CONSPIRATORS OR OTHERWISE THWARTED THEIR SCHEME.

NOW WHAT ABOUT DR. SYNTHCORE AND THE SUIT?

REMEMBER, DR. S. THOUGHT HE WAS CONSPIRING WITH ANOTHER CRIMINAL, BUT IN FACT IT WAS A FEDERAL AGENT.

THE AGENT WASN'T REALLY AGREEING TO THE CRIME, JUST PRETENDING. CAN DR. S. BE CHARGED WITH CONSPIRACY ANYWAY?

IS THERE SUCH A THING AS A CONSPIRACY OF **ONE**?  YES!

ALTHOUGH SOME STATES STILL FOLLOW THE OLD COMMON LAW RULE REQUIRING TWO REAL CONSPIRATORS, MOST JURISDICTIONS THESE DAYS WILL LET DR. S. BE CHARGED WITH CONSPIRACY, UNDER THE THINKING THAT **HE** AT ANY RATE HAD AGREED TO COMMIT THE CRIME.

ONE LAST THING...
...WHAT ABOUT THE BULLET IN THE BABY?

THERE'S AN OFFSHOOT OF ACCOMPLICE LIABILITY CALLED **FELONY MURDER**, WHICH MOST STATES ARE GOING TO APPLY IN THIS CASE.

THE RULE VARIES FROM STATE TO STATE, BUT IN ESSENCE IT SAYS THAT IF YOU'RE PARTICIPATING IN A SERIOUS CRIME (A FELONY), AND SOMEONE GETS KILLED DURING THAT CRIME, THEN YOU WILL BE LIABLE FOR *MURDER*, NO MATTER WHO DID THE ACTUAL KILLING, SO LONG AS EITHER:

1) THE CRIME WAS DANGEROUS TO BEGIN WITH

OR

2) THE DEATH WAS FORESEEABLE.

SO THE QUESTION BECOMES WHETHER THE HEIST WAS INHERENTLY DANGEROUS TO BEGIN WITH, OR WHETHER THE SHOOTING WAS FORESEEABLE.

LET'S SAY NOBODY BUT BAHR KNEW HE'D BROUGHT A GUN ALONG. THE PLAN WAS TO SLIP IN AND SLIP OUT WITHOUT ANYONE REALIZING IT.

ALL BAHR WAS SUPPOSED TO DO WAS ALERT US SO WE COULD ESCAPE.

THE SCHEME DIDN'T PUT ANYONE IN DANGER, AND NOBODY BUT BAHR COULD HAVE FORESEEN THE SHOOTING. IN THAT CASE, MAYBE *BAHR* IS LIABLE FOR THE BABY'S DEATH, BUT THE REST OF US SHOULDN'T BE.

BUT WHAT IF BAHR'S GUN WAS PART OF THE PLAN?

THAT'D MEAN WE HAD ANTICIPATED A SCENARIO WHERE HE'D HAVE TO USE IT. PEOPLE WHO GET SHOT DO SOMETIMES DIE, SO WE COULD CERTAINLY FORESEE A SITUATION WHERE SOMEONE GOT KILLED DURING THE HEIST.

SO IN THAT CASE, WE'D ALL BE GUILTY OF FELONY MURDER.

THAT USUALLY COMES UP IN CASES LIKE AN ARMED ROBBERY, WHERE ONE OF THE ROBBERS GETS KILLED, AND THE OTHER GETS CHARGED WITH HIS MURDER.

ANYWAY, ENOUGH OF THIS.

THE HEIST FAILED, AND IT LOOKS LIKE WE'RE ALL GOING TO JAIL FOR A WHILE — MAYBE YOU KNOW A GOOD DEFENSE LAWYER?

NOW *WOULD* BE A GOOD TIME TO START TALKING ABOUT DEFENSES, WOULDN'T IT?

THEN LET'S KEEP GOING...

"EXCUSE ME!"

JULIE IS A
LOCAL FARMER.

HER MAIN CROP,
BRUSSELS SPROUTS,
HASN'T BEEN
SELLING VERY WELL
(BECAUSE YUCK).

AFTER HEARING THAT SOME STATES
WERE RELAXING THEIR MARIJUANA LAWS,
JULIE MISTAKENLY GOT IT INTO HER HEAD
THAT *HER* STATE HAD LEGALIZED POT.
SO SHE REPLACED HER CROPS WITH
MORE PROFITABLE FIELDS OF DOPE.

TO HER GREAT SURPRISE, JULIE WAS ARRESTED AND CHARGED WITH MARIJUANA CULTIVATION, AND IS NOW FACING A MINIMUM OF 10 YEARS IN PRISON.

BUT I THOUGHT IT WAS LEGAL!

SHE'S A GOOD, LAW-ABIDING PERSON WHO SINCERELY BELIEVED IT WASN'T AGAINST THE LAW. SHE'D NEVER CHOOSE TO COMMIT A CRIME. SHE WAS SIMPLY *MISTAKEN.*

SHOULDN'T SHE BE EXCUSED FROM PUNISHMENT HERE?

NOPE.

IT'S LIKE THEY SAY...

IGNORANCE OF THE LAW IS NO EXCUSE.

IN OTHER WORDS, A MISTAKE OF **LAW** WILL **NOT** EXCUSE YOU FROM CRIMINAL LIABILITY.

THERE ARE **OTHER** KINDS OF SITUATIONS, HOWEVER, WHERE YOU MIGHT BE EXCUSED. SITUATIONS WHERE YOU DID SOMETHING THAT ORDINARILY WOULD HAVE BEEN PUNISHABLE AS A CRIME — BUT INSTEAD YOU'RE OFF THE HOOK.

IN SOME CASES, WHAT YOU DID WAS BAD, BUT YOU'RE **EXCUSED** FOR ONE REASON OR ANOTHER.

THE STATE FORGIVES YOU.

IN OTHER CASES, WHAT YOU DID WASN'T BAD AT ALL — YOU WERE **JUSTIFIED** IN DOING IT.

THERE'S NOTHING TO FORGIVE!

WHAT'S THE DIFFERENCE?

IN CASES WHERE YOU'RE *EXCUSED*, YOU'LL FIND THAT YOU HAD A *CHOICE*. YOU CHOSE TO COMMIT AN OTHERWISE CRIMINAL ACT, BUT UNDER CIRCUMSTANCES THAT MADE IT THE SOCIALLY ACCEPTABLE CHOICE.

IN CASES WHERE YOU'RE *JUSTIFIED*, THE LAW SAYS YOU HAD *NO* CHOICE. YOU COMMITTED AN OTHERWISE CRIMINAL ACT, BUT UNDER CIRCUMSTANCES WHERE SOCIETY SAYS THERE WAS NO OTHER OPTION.

LET'S SEE HOW THESE PLAY OUT.

YOU KNOW THAT MISTAKE OF LAW IS NO DEFENSE, BUT HOW ABOUT MISTAKE OF **FACT**?

SAMANTHA HERE, FOR EXAMPLE, WAS AT HER WATERING HOLE DRINKING FOR FREE AS USUAL. THE GUY AT THE END OF THE BAR MUST HAVE BOUGHT HER THREE OR FOUR FUNKYTINIS THAT NIGHT.

EXCEPT HE HADN'T. HE'D BEEN PAYING FOR THE GIRL SITTING NEXT TO HER. AND WHEN SAMANTHA LEFT THE BAR WITHOUT PAYING, THE BARTENDER CALLED THE COPS ON HER.

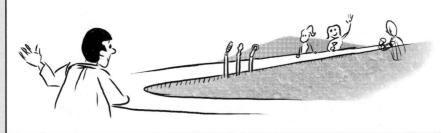

IT HAD BEEN A REASONABLE MISTAKE, THOUGH. FROM THAT ANGLE, IT SURE LOOKED LIKE SHE WAS THE INTENDED RECIPIENT, AND SHE WASN'T TRYING TO STEAL DRINKS FROM THE BAR.

SAMANTHA'S WAS A MISTAKE OF **FACT**.

SOME AUTHORITIES SAY HER MISTAKE GIVES HER A DEFENSE TO THE CHARGE OF BOOZE THEFT. BUT THEY ARE **WRONG**.

A DEFENSE IS SOMETHING THAT LETS YOU GET AWAY WITH SOMETHING THAT'S ORDINARILY A **CRIME**. MISTAKE OF FACT, ON THE OTHER HAND, IS ONLY USEFUL AS EVIDENCE THAT YOU DIDN'T HAVE THE NECESSARY MENS REA — IN OTHER WORDS, THAT THERE WAS **NO CRIME** IN THE **FIRST PLACE**.

SO MISTAKE OF LAW IS NO DEFENSE, AND MISTAKE OF FACT ISN'T REALLY ONE, EITHER.

GAH! IT'S ENOUGH TO MAKE YOU CRAZY!

GOOD IDEA. FOR THE TIME BEING, ANYWAY. SO HOW ABOUT A LITTLE TEMPORARY INSANITY?

WELL, MAYBE JUST A SMIDGE.

LET'S BE A BIT MORE PRECISE, THOUGH.

WHEN PEOPLE USE THE PHRASE "TEMPORARY INSANITY," WHAT THEY'RE REALLY TALKING ABOUT IS THE DEFENSE OF *PROVOCATION*.

HOW INCITEFUL!

AAAANYWAY...

FRED CAME HOME ONE DAY TO FIND HIS WIFE IN BED WITH THE PLUMBER.

THE SHOCK *ENRAGED* HIM SO THAT HE COULD BARELY SEE, AND HE LEAPT ONTO THE BED AND STARTED PUMMELING THE PLUMBER.

ONE OF THE BLOWS CRUSHED HIS WINDPIPE, AND THE PLUMBER *DIED*.

FRED WAS CHARGED WITH MURDERING THE PLUMBER.

AT TRIAL, HE ASSERTED A PROVOCATION DEFENSE, CLAIMING THAT HE WAS IN A MURDEROUS RAGE FOR A DARN GOOD REASON, AND SO HE MUST THEREFORE BE EXCUSED.

IT'S NOT THAT I WAS INSANE AT THE TIME...

JUST THAT YOU CAN'T BLAME ME FOR REACTING THE WAY I DID!

WITNESS

SO HE'S GOING TO NEED THE JURY TO BELIEVE THAT:

1 THE PLUMBER *PROVOKED* HIM,

2 INTO A PASSION THAT *OVERCAME* HIS REASON,

3 HE KILLED IN THE *HEAT* OF THAT PASSION, AND

4 A "*REASONABLE PERSON*" IN THAT SITUATION WOULD HAVE BEEN JUST AS PROVOKED.

NOW, NOT EVERY STATE ALLOWS THIS DEFENSE. AND EVEN IN THE ONES THAT DO ALLOW IT, IT'S **NOT** A COMPLETE DEFENSE — ALL IT DOES IS KNOCK A MURDER CHARGE DOWN TO A LESSER **MANSLAUGHTER.**

DUDE, TAKE SOME ANGER MANAGEMENT CLASSES, ALREADY!

THE RATIONALE HERE IS THAT SOCIETY DOESN'T THINK IT'S AS BAD AS MURDER, IF YOU KILL SOMEONE WHO BROUGHT IT ON **HIMSELF,** SOMEONE WHO DID SOMETHING SO OUTRAGEOUS THAT IT WOULD HAVE CAUSED **ANYONE** TO BECOME SO ENRAGED THAT THEY WOULD HAVE LOST CONTROL.

TV AND MOVIES ASIDE, HOWEVER, THIS DEFENSE DOESN'T COME UP ALL THAT MUCH IN REAL LIFE.

 ≠

AND WHEN IT DOES, JURIES **RARELY** GO FOR IT. THEY USED TO A HUNDRED YEARS AGO, BUT NOT ANYMORE.

WHY?

LET'S GO BACK TO THAT PHRASE **"REASONABLE PERSON."** IT'S USED A LOT IN THE LAW. IN THIS DEFENSE, YOU'D NEED THE JURY TO BELIEVE THAT A REASONABLE PERSON — NOT JUST THE ACCUSED PERSON — WOULD HAVE BEEN EQUALLY PROVOKED.

IT'S AN "OBJECTIVE TEST."

(WHEN YOU'RE CONCERNED WITH WHAT THE ACCUSED WAS ACTUALLY THINKING, WE SAY YOU'RE BEING **SUBJECTIVE.**

WHEN YOU'RE CONCERNED INSTEAD WITH WHAT SOME HYPOTHETICAL **REASONABLE PERSON** WOULD HAVE THOUGHT IN THAT SITUATION, YOU'RE BEING **OBJECTIVE.**)

LEGAL THEORISTS HAVE TRIED FOR GENERATIONS TO COME UP WITH A DEFINITION OF "REASONABLE PERSON" THAT JURIES COULD APPLY. BUT **IN REAL LIFE**, WHEN A JUROR IS ASKED TO THINK OF WHAT A REASONABLE PERSON WOULD HAVE DONE, HE SIMPLY ASKS IF **HE** WOULD HAVE ACTED THAT WAY **HIMSELF.**

IN OTHER WORDS, THE THEORETICAL "REASONABLE PERSON" IN PRACTICE IS SIMPLY THE JURY ITSELF.

SO WHAT A JURY THINKS IS REASONABLE IS GOING TO VARY FROM PLACE TO PLACE, AND OVER TIME, AS ATTITUDES CHANGE AND *EVOLVE.*

THE DEFENSE OF PROVOCATION IS ONE THAT SEEMS TO BE EVOLVING OUT OF EXISTENCE. FEWER AND FEWER PEOPLE WOULD THINK *THEMSELVES* EXCUSED FOR KILLING SOMEONE WHO MERELY GOT THEM REALLY UPSET. SO FEWER AND FEWER JURIES WILL EXCUSE SOMEONE *ELSE* FOR DOING IT.

SO PROVOCATION RARELY WORKS ANYMORE; AND WHEN IT DOES, IT'S NOT EVEN A COMPLETE DEFENSE (AGAIN, IT'S ONLY AVAILABLE IN MURDER CASES, AND ONLY REDUCES THE CHARGE TO MANSLAUGHTER).

INSANITY, ON THE OTHER HAND, **IS** A COMPLETE DEFE

STOP RIGHT THERE. THAT'S A VERY INSENSITIVE TERM. I PREFER YOU SAY "HAVING A PSYCHIATRIC ILLNESS OR EMOTIONAL DISABILITY."

NO, INSANITY IS ACTUALLY THE RIGHT WORD TO USE. IT'S NOT A MEDICAL TERM OR ONE OF THE EVER-CHANGING PC EUPHEMISMS FOR MENTAL DISORDER.

THIS MAY SOUND CRAZY, BUT THE TERM "INSANITY" IS NOT A PSYCHIATRIC DIAGNOSIS, BUT A **LEGAL CONCLUSION.** IT'S DETERMINED NOT BY DOCTORS, BUT BY JURORS.

WHEN THE LAW SAYS YOU'RE INSANE, THAT MEANS YOU AREN'T ABLE TO UNDERSTAND THAT WHAT YOU'RE DOING IS WRONG.

NOT SO MUCH THIS...

...AS THIS:

REALITY

VARIOUS STATES USE SLIGHTLY DIFFERENT DEFINITIONS, BUT THEY ALL BASICALLY MEAN AN INABILITY TO UNDERSTAND WHAT YOU WERE DOING, OR THAT IT WAS WRONG, BECAUSE OF SOME MENTAL PROBLEM.

DOUGLAS, FOR EXAMPLE, HAS A CHEMICAL IMBALANCE IN HIS BRAIN THAT MAKES HIM DELUSIONAL. ONE DAY, HE WAS WALKING DOWN THE STREET, WHEN OUT OF NOWHERE A DRAGON TRIED TO EAT HIM.

THINKING QUICKLY, DOUGLAS GRABBED A NEARBY PIPE, WHACKED THE DRAGON UPSIDE THE HEAD, AND RAN AWAY SCREAMING IN TERROR.

POW!

SADLY, WHAT HE'D THOUGHT TO BE A DRAGON TURNED OUT TO BE TINA...

AND NOW SHE'S DEAD.

DOUGLAS KILLED TINA, NO QUESTION.

HE INTENDED TO KILL HER, OR AT LEAST CAUSE HER SEVERE PHYSICAL INJURY.

UNDER HIS STATE'S LAW, HE HAD THE NECESSARY MENS REA AND COMMITTED THE NECESSARY ACTUS REUS TO BE CHARGED WITH *MURDER.*

EVEN SO, WE'RE *NOT* GOING TO PUNISH HIM FOR IT.

DOUGLAS IS EXCUSED, BECAUSE IN HIS CONDITION HE COULDN'T HAVE KNOWN THAT HE WAS KILLING TINA.

REMEMBER, WE ONLY WANT TO PUNISH PEOPLE WHO *DESERVE* IT. SOMEONE WHO DIDN'T KNOW WHAT HE WAS DOING MAY NEED *TREATMENT,* BUT PUNISHMENT WOULD SERVE NO *PURPOSE.*

SO IF INSANITY IS PROVED, THE DEFENDANT CANNOT BE FOUND GUILTY.

BUT THAT DOESN'T MEAN HE SIMPLY GOES FREE, MOST OF THE TIME.

HE MIGHT HAVE TO BE **COMMITTED** TO A MENTAL INSTITUTION UNTIL HE'S NO LONGER A DANGER TO HIMSELF OR OTHERS, BUT THAT'S AN ACT OF *CIVIL* LAW, NOT CRIMINAL LAW.

WHO HAS TO PROVE IT?

IN MOST STATES AND IN FEDERAL COURT, INSANITY MUST BE PROVED BY THE *DEFENDANT.*

AND WHAT'S RELEVANT IS THE DEFENDANT'S MENTAL STATE AT THE TIME OF THE OFFENSE. (WHETHER HE'S MENTALLY COMPETENT TO STAND TRIAL NOW, OR TO BE PUNISHED LATER, ARE SEPARATE ISSUES.)

IN REAL LIFE, INSANITY DEFENSES ARE ALMOST NEVER RAISED.

AND THEY ALMOST NEVER SUCCEED.

SO KEEP ALL THIS IN PERSPECTIVE.

PEOPLE ARE MORE LIKELY TO TRY THE RELATED DEFENSE OF **DIMINISHED CAPACITY.**

 THOUGH IT'S RARELY A WINNER, EITHER.

DIMINISHED CAPACITY IS WHEN YOU DIDN'T HAVE A MENTAL PROBLEM, SO YOU WEREN'T LEGALLY INSANE, BUT SOMETHING **ELSE** MADE YOU UNABLE TO UNDERSTAND WHAT YOU WERE DOING, OR THAT IT WAS WRONG.

THIS DEFENSE ALMOST ALWAYS **FAILS,** BECAUSE USUALLY IT'S THE DEFENDANT HIMSELF WHO'S AT FAULT FOR BEING IN THAT CONDITION IN THE FIRST PLACE.

TAKE BRIAN, FOR EXAMPLE.
HE GOT SO LIQUORED UP AT LUANNE'S PARTY
THAT HE **BLACKED OUT.** WHEN HE CAME
TO THE NEXT DAY, HE LEARNED THAT HE HAD
SOMEHOW DRUNKENLY RAPED LUANNE.

IT'S ALL ON VIDEO, YOU CREEP!

HIS INTOXICATION CERTAINLY PREVENTED
HIM FROM KNOWING WHAT HE WAS DOING,
BUT THAT'S NOT GOING TO BE A DEFENSE,
BECAUSE **HE'S** THE ONE WHO
GOT HIMSELF DRUNK.

BRIAN WAS DRINKING INTENTIONALLY
(OR RECKLESSLY), SO WE'RE BASICALLY
APPLYING THAT MENS REA TO WHATEVER
HE DID WHILE INTOXICATED.

MAYBE IF SOMEONE HELD HIM
DOWN AND FORCED A WHOLE
BOTTLE OF BOURBON DOWN
HIS THROAT, AGAINST HIS
WILL, BUT SUCH THINGS DON'T
HAPPEN IN REAL LIFE.

 FIRST MY MAGUFFIN, NOW THIS?
IS THIS HOMAGE OR THEFT?

 THAT'S A DIFFERENT
AREA OF LAW.

SIMILARLY, WHAT IF DOUG HAD THOUGHT THAT TINA WAS A DRAGON, NOT BECAUSE OF A SCHIZOPHRENIC DELUSION, BUT BECAUSE HE WAS *HIGH* ON HALLUCINOGENS?

IF HE TOOK THE DRUGS ON PURPOSE, THEN THAT INTENT IS GOING TO BE TRANSFERRED TO WHAT HE DID TO TINA. HE'S GUILTY OF MURDER.

BUT IF HIS DOCTOR HAD GIVEN THEM TO HIM BY MISTAKE? THEN YEAH, HE MIGHT HAVE A VALID DIMINISHED CAPACITY DEFENSE.

IF, THAT IS, THE DEFENSE IS EVEN RECOGNIZED IN HIS STATE ANYMORE. SOME JURISDICTIONS HAVE *ABOLISHED* THE DIMINISHED CAPACITY DEFENSE.

AND OTHERS DEFINE IT DIFFERENTLY.

SO IN REAL LIFE, DOUG MIGHT NOT HAVE A VALID DEFENSE EVEN THEN.

SO FAR, WE'VE COVERED SEVERAL EXCUSE DEFENSES THAT YOU HEAR ABOUT A LOT, BUT THAT *RARELY* COME UP IN REAL LIFE,

AND THAT ALMOST *NEVER* SUCCEED.

BUT BEFORE WE MOVE ON TO JUSTIFICATION DEFENSES, THERE IS ONE EXCUSE THAT YOU HEAR ABOUT THAT *DOES* COME UP IN REAL LIFE.

AND IT'S ONE THAT PEOPLE GET WRONG *ALL THE TIME.*

SO HOW ABOUT WE LEARN HOW TO GET IT RIGHT?

OKAY!

"I WAS ENTRAPPED!"

MEET CORA THE
CALL GIRL.

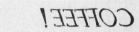

SHE'S VERY CAREFUL
NOT TO GET CAUGHT.

SO SHE ADVERTISES
ANONYMOUSLY...

WORKS STRICTLY
SOLO...

AND ASKS MENTORS FOR ADVICE.

NEVER CARRY CONDOMS. THE POLICE THINK THEY'RE EVIDENCE OF PROSTITUTION AND YOU'LL GET ARRESTED.

THAT'S POSSIBLY THE **DUMBEST** ADVICE I'VE EVER HEARD.

(NOT THAT SHE NECESSARILY TAKES IT.)

ALSO, WHENEVER SHE GOES OUT ON A CALL...

HEY CORA!

HEY JOE!

...SHE ALWAYS MAKES SURE TO **ASK** IF THE GUY IS A **COP** OR NOT, FIRST.

YESTERDAY, CORA TOOK HER USUAL PRECAUTIONS, MADE SURE THE CUSTOMER WASN'T A COP...

NOW IN JAIL, SHE TELLS HER LAWYER IT'S OUTRAGEOUS.

GRAYSON ISN'T A DRUG DEALER, BUT HE KNOWS ONE OR TWO AROUND THE NEIGHBORHOOD.

YEAH, PETER PROVIDES FOR THE POTHEADS, AND HARRY HANDLES THE HEROIN.

ONE DAY, A DEALER FROM OUT OF TOWN OFFERED HIM A WAD OF CASH IF HE'D DELIVER A HAVERSACK OF HEROIN TO HARRY.

I FEEL SAFER THIS WAY. HE KNOWS YOU, AFTER ALL.

GRAYSON TOOK THE CASH, DELIVERED THE BAG,

AND IMMEDIATELY GOT ARRESTED.

THAT SO-CALLED "DEALER" WAS REALLY AN UNDERCOVER COP. NOW GRAYSON'S LOOKING AT YEARS IN PRISON, AND HE'S TRYING TO CONVINCE HIS LAWYER THAT HE SHOULD WALK.

HEY, IT WASN'T MY IDEA TO DO IT. THE POLICE **THEMSELVES** ASKED ME TO DO IT!

SYLVESTER USED TO BE A STREET DEALER BACK IN THE DAY, BUT HE GOT SMART. NOW HIS OPERATION IS COMPLETELY HIDDEN FROM THE POLICE.

HE OWNS TWO BUILDINGS ON THE BLOCK, AND EVERYONE INSIDE WORKS FOR HIM.

MY SECURITY IS FANTASTIC.

AND HE ONLY SELLS WHOLESALE, TO OTHER KNOWN DEALERS.

NO UNDERCOVERS ARE GETTING INSIDE THIS OPERATION.

ONE OF HIS YOUNG PROTÉGÉS, SOLID SAUL, IS ONE OF HIS MOST **TRUSTED** WORKERS. FOR **TWO YEARS** NOW, SAUL HAS PROVED HIS VALUE TIME AND AGAIN, SO SYLVESTER GAVE HIM HIS OWN SPOT TO RUN — AN APARTMENT WHERE SAUL WILL BE RESPONSIBLE FOR MOVING TWO KILOS PER WEEK.

I'M SO PROUD OF YOU, SOLLIE.

A FEW DAYS LATER, TWO BUSLOADS OF COPS **RAIDED** SYLVESTER'S BUILDINGS, ARRESTING EVERYBODY.

EVEN GRANDMA?

WELL, SHE **IS** MY BEST LOOKOUT...

IT SEEMS THAT SAUL WAS AN UNDERCOVER COP THE **WHOLE TIME!** AND NOW SYLVESTER'S BEING PROSECUTED FOR THE KILOS THAT **SAUL** WAS GOING TO SELL.

(CONSPIRACY, ACCOMPLICE LIABILITY, AND ALL THAT.)

NO WAY. THE **POLICE** CAN'T BREAK THE LAW AND THEN CHARGE ME WITH THEIR **OWN** CRIME.

JEN, HERE, IS ONE ANGRY ANARCHIST. FOR MONTHS NOW, SHE'S BEEN PLOTTING TO ASSASSINATE THE MAYOR.

USING HER UNDERGROUND CONNECTIONS, SHE BEGAN SHOPPING FOR THE RIGHT KIND OF WEAPON.

AFTER A WHILE, SHE WAS INTRODUCED TO LORRIE, AN ARMS DEALER WHO HAD JUST THE THING.

IT'S A SUPER SILENT SHARP SHOOTING SECRET SNIPER RIFLE!

JEN HAPPILY BOUGHT THE WEAPON FROM LORRIE.

HER PLAN WAS COMING TOGETHER VERY NICELY.

SQUEE!

SMARMI

EXCEPT FOR THE PART WHERE THE FEDS LOCKED HER UP.

YEAH, THAT PART SUCKED.

HERE'S SOME MORE BAD NEWS: I'M AN UNDERCOVER AGENT — THE WHOLE THING WAS A CLASSIC STING.

WHAT?

YOU MEAN THE FEDS ACTUALLY *HELPED* ME COMMIT THE CRIME?

I WAS *ENTRAPPED!*

ERG!

AT THE OTHER END OF THE SOCIAL PROTEST SPECTRUM, ZEKE WAS MARCHING WITH THOUSANDS OF OUTRAGED CITIZENS TO PROTEST THE MAYOR'S LATEST ATROCITY.

AS THE MARCH APPROACHED THE CITY HALL BRIDGE, ZEKE SAW DOZENS OF POLICE IN RIOT GEAR LINING THE ROADWAY.

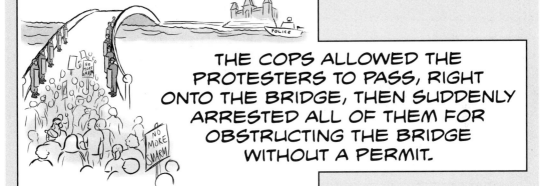

THE COPS ALLOWED THE PROTESTERS TO PASS, RIGHT ONTO THE BRIDGE, THEN SUDDENLY ARRESTED ALL OF THEM FOR OBSTRUCTING THE BRIDGE WITHOUT A PERMIT.

ZEKE IS CERTAIN THAT THAT WASN'T RIGHT.

THE POLICE DIDN'T EVEN *TRY* TO STOP US.

THEY CAN'T JUST LET YOU BREAK THE LAW...

I WAS *ENTRAPPED!*

OH FOR CRYING OUT...

TO EACH OF THESE DEFENDANTS, THEIR LAWYER HAS ONLY ONE THING TO SAY:

EACH OF HER CLIENTS HAS FALLEN FOR ONE OF THE COMMON MYTHS ABOUT ENTRAPMENT.

AND ALL OF THEM ARE WRONG!!

MYTH #1: A COP HAS TO TELL YOU IF HE'S A COP.

FALSE.
NO UNDERCOVER COP EVER HAS TO ADMIT HE'S A POLICE OFFICER.

BUT EVERYONE KNOWS THEY HAVE TO!

WELL, EVERYBODY'S **WRONG.**

IT'S AMAZING THAT THIS MYTH HAS STUCK AROUND SO LONG, WHEN TONS OF UNDERCOVER ARRESTS PROVE IT WRONG EVERY DAY.

I STILL DON'T GET IT. I'VE HEARD IT A THOUSAND TIMES FROM KIDS AT SCHOOL, IN MOVIES, ON TV.

WELL, MAYBE IT'S NOT SO AMAZING AFTER ALL.

REGARDLESS, WITHOUT DECEPTION, THE POLICE COULDN'T DO THEIR JOB VERY WELL.

IF SOMEONE KNOWS I'M A COP, THEY'RE NOT LIKELY TO LET ME CATCH THEM IN THE **ACT,** ARE THEY?

AND OF COURSE THERE ARE OTHER
REASONS WHY AN UNDERCOVER OFFICER
SHOULDN'T HAVE TO ADMIT IT.

ESSENTIALLY, IT'S THIS:

IF...

1 THE POLICE **CAUSED** YOU TO COMMIT A CRIME

AND...

2 YOU WOULDN'T HAVE COMMITTED IT OTHERWISE,

THEN...

3 YOU WERE **ENTRAPPED.**

ENTRAPMENT IS CONCERNED WITH WHETHER THE POLICE (THE STATE) *CORRUPTED* YOU TO COMMIT A CRIME YOU WEREN'T OTHERWISE INCLINED TO COMMIT.

A COMMON THEME YOU'RE GOING TO COME ACROSS IN AMERICAN CRIMINAL LAW IS THAT WE DON'T LIKE THE STATE TO OVERRIDE YOUR FREE WILL, AND FORCE YOU TO GET *YOURSELF* IN TROUBLE.

JUST WAIT'LL WE COVER CONFESSIONS AND SEARCHES (IN CRIMINAL PROCEDURE).

NOTE, HOWEVER, THAT ENTRAPMENT DOES NOT MEAN THE POLICE FORCED YOU TO COMMIT THE OFFENSE.

IT'S MORE THAT THEY *TRICKED* YOU INTO IT.

ENTRAPMENT IS AN "EXCUSE" DEFENSE, WHERE YOU HAD A CHOICE, BUT YOU NEVER WOULD HAVE CHOSEN AS YOU DID IF THE POLICE HADN'T CHANGED YOUR MIND.

THIS IS A "SUBJECTIVE" APPROACH, ASKING WHETHER THE DEFENDANT HERSELF WAS ALREADY PREDISPOSED TO COMMIT THE CRIME.

IT'S ALL ABOUT FAIRNESS TO THIS PARTICULAR PERSON WHO'S BEING ACCUSED.

BUT BE AWARE THAT A FEW STATES USE AN "OBJECTIVE" APPROACH — ASKING INSTEAD WHETHER THE POLICE ACTION WOULD HAVE CORRUPTED *ANY* LAW-ABIDING CITIZEN.

INSTEAD OF FAIRNESS, THIS APPROACH IS ALL ABOUT DETERRING BAD POLICE CONDUCT.

IT DOESN'T MATTER WHICH TEST IS APPLIED TO CORA, HOWEVER. SHE WAS ALREADY PERFECTLY *WILLING* TO ENGAGE IN PROSTITUTION. THE UNDERCOVER COP DIDN'T HAVE ANYTHING TO DO WITH THAT.

AND HE DIDN'T DO ANYTHING THAT WOULD HAVE MADE A REGULAR JANE TAKE UP THE PROFESSION *AGAINST* HER OWN PRINCIPLES.

SO CAN WE STOP TALKING ABOUT ENTRAPMENT, CORA, AND PLEASE FOCUS ON WHAT I *CAN* MAYBE DO TO HELP YOU?

AND AS FOR THE *REST* OF YOU...

MYTH #2: THE POLICE CANNOT ASK YOU TO COMMIT A CRIME.

MYTH #3: THE POLICE CAN'T BREAK THE LAW THEMSELVES.

(THERE ARE LIMITS ON WHAT CRIMES UNDERCOVERS CAN ENGAGE IN. THEY CAN'T HURT SOMEONE, FOR EXAMPLE, OR CONDUCT ILLEGAL WIRETAPS OR OTHERWISE VIOLATE THEIR TARGETS' CONSTITUTIONAL RIGHTS.

BUT THEY ARE ALLOWED TO COMMIT CRIMES INCIDENTAL TO THEIR UNDERCOVER ROLE. SO A COP POSING AS AN ADDICT IS ALLOWED TO BUY AND POSSESS DRUGS. AND SAUL WAS ALLOWED TO DO SO IN HIS ROLE AS DEALER.)

MYTH #4: THE POLICE CAN'T HELP YOU BREAK THE LAW.

SORRY, JEN, BUT THIS IS JUST THE FLIP SIDE OF MYTH #3.

YOU WERE ALREADY **TRYING** TO COMMIT THE CRIME.

GIVING YOU THE **MEANS** TO DO IT SIMPLY CONFIRMED YOUR INTENT. IT DIDN'T **CREATE** A DESIRE YOU DIDN'T ALREADY HAVE.

ONE OF LAW ENFORCEMENT'S MORE IMPORTANT TOOLS FOR ROOTING OUT ASSASSINS, TERROR CELLS, AND OTHER PLOTS IS THE USE OF THE **AGENT PROVOCATEUR** — TYPICALLY AN UNDERCOVER OR INFORMANT WHO POSES AS A SYMPATHIZER OR A SUPPLIER IN ORDER TO IDENTIFY THREATS AND GATHER EVIDENCE.

DESPITE THE NEGATIVE CONNOTATIONS ASSOCIATED WITH THE TERM, MERELY **USING** PROVOCATEURS ISN'T A PROBLEM.

IT ONLY BECOMES A PROBLEM WHEN THE PROVOCATEUR ACTUALLY **ENTRAPS** AN INNOCENT PERSON — WHICH DIDN'T HAPPEN HERE.

FINALLY, THERE'S **MYTH #5:** THE POLICE CAN'T JUST LET YOU COMMIT AN OFFENSE AND THEN ARREST YOU FOR IT.

SORRY, ZEKE, BUT IT WAS YOUR DECISION TO BLOCK THE BRIDGE.

I KNOW WHERE YOU'RE GOING WITH THIS, BUT MY CASE IS **DIFFERENT.**

WHEN THE POLICE JUST STOOD THERE AND LET US GO ON THE BRIDGE, THEY LED ME TO BELIEVE THAT IT WAS **OKAY,** THAT WE WEREN'T DOING ANYTHING WRONG — I'M A LAW-ABIDING CITIZEN!

SORRY, ZEKE, BUT THAT'S STILL **NOT ENTRAPMENT.** MAYBE WE HAVE A MISTAKE DEFENSE (I'LL HAVE TO READ HOW THE ORDINANCE IS WRITTEN). BUT AS FOR ENTRAPMENT, YOU WERE ALREADY INCLINED TO BLOCK THE BRIDGE. THE COPS ONLY GAVE YOU THE **OPPORTUNITY** TO DO SO.

SO WHAT *WOULD* COUNT AS ENTRAPMENT?

LET'S SEE:

FRANCINE IS A NICE, LAWFUL YOUNG PHYSICIST AT A GOVERNMENT LAB.

YOU LEFT OUT "SMART" AND "BEAUTIFUL."

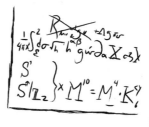

HER PAL GLENN OFFERS HER TEN THOUSAND DOLLARS IF SHE'LL COPY SOME FILES FOR HIM.

SHE REFUSES.

GLENN PLEADS WITH HER: HE'S IN OVER HIS HEAD WITH SOME VERY BAD PEOPLE, AND THEY'RE GOING TO KILL HIM IF HE DOESN'T GET THEM THOSE FILES.

FRANCINE IS SHOCKED, BUT THIS IS HER PAL'S LIFE AT STAKE. AND THE FILES AREN'T ALL THAT IMPORTANT...

OKAY.

AFTER FRANCINE IS ARRESTED FOR ESPIONAGE, SHE LEARNS THAT GLENN HAD REALLY BEEN IN A WHOLE 'NOTHER KIND OF TROUBLE.

IT SEEMS THAT HE HAD BEEN CAUGHT SELLING SECRETS.

TO GET A LIGHTER SENTENCE, HE'D OFFERED TO COOPERATE WITH THE FEDS AND HELP THEM CATCH OTHER SPIES.

BUT HE DIDN'T ACTUALLY KNOW ANY OTHER SPIES. SO, LIKE COUNTLESS INFORMANTS BEFORE HIM, HE TRIED TO GET SOMEBODY — ANYBODY — ELSE IN TROUBLE.

HEY, BETTER YOU THAN *ME*, BUDDY.

GLENN WAS ACTING ON THE GOVERNMENT'S BEHALF, SO IT COUNTS AS POLICE ACTION. AND WHAT HE DID WAS ABSOLUTELY ENTRAPMENT.

THE CLASSIC EXAMPLE OF A *BAD* AGENT PROVOCATEUR.

FRANCINE WAS IN NO WAY PREDISPOSED TO SELL SECRETS. IT WAS ONLY AFTER HE **OVERCAME** HER **RESISTANCE** THAT SHE GAVE IN AND CHANGED HER MIND.

AND ZEKE, IF YOU HAD GONE UP TO THE COPS AND **ASKED** THEM IF IT WOULD BE OKAY, AND THEY HAD SAID YES, YOU'D HAVE A DEFENSE.

THEN THEY WOULD HAVE ENTRAPPED YOU BY THEIR **FALSE REPRESENTATION.**

NOW YOU TELL ME.

ANYHOO, THAT'S THAT FOR ENTRAPMENT. AND THAT'S THE LAST OF THE "EXCUSE" DEFENSES.

WAIT...

SO NEXT TIME, WE'LL TALK ABOUT THE "JUSTIFICATION" DEFENSES OF...

WAIT!

WHAT ABOUT DURESS? ISN'T THAT ONE OF THE STANDARD EXCUSE DEFENSES?

WELL, LET'S SEE...

"I HAD TO DO IT!"

REMEMBER, THERE ARE TWO TYPES OF DEFENSES:

"EXCUSE DEFENSES"

WHERE SOCIETY WOULD **PREFER** YOU HADN'T DONE IT, BUT STILL ISN'T GOING TO **PUNISH** YOU FOR IT.

AND "JUSTIFICATION" DEFENSES

DING!

WHERE SOCIETY SAYS YOU ACTUALLY DID THE **RIGHT THING.**

IF YOU HAD OTHER OPTIONS, THEN IT'S AN "EXCUSE" DEFENSE, SUCH AS EXTREME PROVOCATION ...

FONDLE MY KID, WILL YOU!?

LEGAL INSANITY...

OR ENTRAPMENT.

BUT IF YOU HAD **NO** CHOICE,
THEN IT'S A "JUSTIFICATION" DEFENSE.

BUT DOES ANYONE EVER REALLY HAVE **NO** OTHER OPTION?

I MEAN, YOU CAN ALWAYS CHOOSE TO DO **NOTHING,** RIGHT?

YES, BUT WHEN WE SAY YOU HAD NO CHOICE, WE REALLY MEAN THAT YOU DIDN'T HAVE A *SOCIALLY ACCEPTABLE* ALTERNATIVE.

IN OTHER WORDS, DOING NOTHING WOULD HAVE BEEN *WRONG.*

THERE ARE *THREE* MAIN JUSTIFICATION DEFENSES:

1 *NECESSITY –*
WHERE CIRCUMSTANCES COMPELLED YOU TO DO IT, FOR THE GREATER GOOD.

YOU *HAD* TO DO IT.

2 *DURESS –*
WHERE ANOTHER PERSON THREATENED TO HURT YOU, UNLESS YOU DID IT.

HE *MADE* YOU DO IT.

AND...

3 *SELF-DEFENSE –*
WHERE SOMEONE WAS ABOUT TO HURT YOU,* AND YOU HAD TO STOP HIM.

HE MADE YOU DO IT TO *HIM.*

*OR SOMEONE ELSE.

FIRST, LET'S LOOK AT **NECESSITY**. HOW CAN YOU TELL WHEN CIRCUMSTANCES JUSTIFY COMMITTING AN ACT THAT ORDINARILY WOULD HAVE BEEN A CRIME?

MEET DYLAN THE DIMWIT.

USING GASOLINE AND DYNAMITE, HE BURNED HIS OWN HOUSE DOWN SO HE COULD COLLECT THE INSURANCE MONEY (COMMITTING ARSON AND FRAUD IN HIS STATE).

THE FIRE QUICKLY BEGAN TO SPREAD UP AND DOWN HIS BLOCK.

THE VOLUNTEER FIRE DEPARTMENT NEVER WOULD HAVE MADE IT IN TIME. SOMETHING HAD TO BE DONE FAST, OR ELSE MANY MORE HOMES WOULD BE DESTROYED, AND PEOPLE MIGHT EVEN DIE.

HARRY THE HERO LEAPT INTO ACTION,
EVACUATED THE HOUSE NEXT TO THE FIRE,
AND DEMOLISHED IT TO MAKE A FIREBREAK.

ORDINARILY, DESTROYING SOMEONE'S HOME
LIKE THAT IS A SERIOUS CRIME. BUT WHEN HARRY
THE HERO DID IT, IT WASN'T A CRIME AT ALL.
IT WAS JUSTIFIED BY NECESSITY.

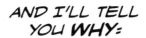

AND I'LL TELL YOU **WHY:**

FIRST, THERE WAS AN IMMEDIATE DANGER...

ACTUALLY, WE NOW KNOW THERE WASN'T. THE WIND WAS BLOWING THE FIRE **AWAY** FROM MY HOUSE!

THAT DOESN'T MATTER.

I BELIEVED THERE **WAS** AN IMMEDIATE DANGER. THAT'S ALL THAT MATTERS.

BUT YOUR BELIEF WAS UNREASONABLE. THE WIND WAS BLOWING REALLY HARD.

IT DOESN'T MATTER IF MY BELIEF WAS UNREASONABLE. ALL THAT MATTERS IS THAT IT WAS **SINCERE.**

SO FIRST, I SINCERELY BELIEVED THERE WAS AN IMMEDIATE DANGER.

SECOND, THE HARM I DID WAS SMALLER THAN THE HARM I TRIED TO PREVENT.

THAT'S WHY THIS IS SOMETIMES CALLED THE "LESSER OF TWO EVILS" DEFENSE.

AND LAST, THERE WAS NO OTHER OPTION THAT WAS LESS SEVERE.

THE FIRE DEPARTMENT WOULDN'T COME IN TIME, AND BLOWING OUT FIRES ISN'T ONE OF MY POWERS.

SO EVEN THOUGH HARRY KNOCKED DOWN SOMEONE'S HOUSE, HE'S NOT GOING TO JAIL. HE HAS A DEFENSE OF NECESSITY, BECAUSE:

1 HE SINCERELY BELIEVED THERE WAS AN IMMEDIATE DANGER.

2 THE HARM HE CAUSED REALLY WAS LESS THAN THE HARM HE WAS TRYING TO PREVENT, AND

3 THERE WAS NO OTHER WAY TO DO IT THAT WAS LESS HARMFUL.

DIDN'T I JUST SAY THAT?

DYLAN THE DIMWIT HAD THE SAME IDEA. GRABBING SOME LEFTOVER TNT, HE EVACUATED AND DEMOLISHED THE HOUSE ON THE OTHER SIDE OF THE BLAZE.

I'M HELPING!

DYLAN SINCERELY (AND CORRECTLY) BELIEVED THERE WAS AN IMMEDIATE DANGER; DESTROYING THE ONE HOME WAS LESS HARM THAN LETTING THE REST BURN DOWN; AND THERE WASN'T A LESS HARMFUL ALTERNATIVE.

SO I'M JUSTIFIED, RIGHT?

NO, YOU'RE GOING TO JAIL.

FOR BURNING DOWN MY **OWN** HOUSE, MAYBE — BUT SURELY NOT FOR KNOCKING DOWN A **NEIGHBOR'S** HOUSE TO SAVE EVERYONE ELSE'S!

WHY CAN'T I CLAIM **NECESSITY**?

BECAUSE THE NECESSITY DEFENSE DOESN'T APPLY IF YOU'RE THE ONE WHO CAUSED THE EMERGENCY IN THE FIRST PLACE.

THERE'S NO SUCH THING AS A CHUTZPAH DEFENSE.

DARN.

SADLY, DYLAN'S DEMOLITION DIDN'T DO THE TRICK. THE BLAZE JUMPED THE FIREBREAK AND THREATENED TO DESTROY THE REST OF THE BLOCK.

BECKY'S PRIZED BENTLEY WAS TRAPPED, OUT OF GAS, IN THE LOT AT THE END OF THE BLOCK.

TO SAVE IT FROM DESTRUCTION, BECKY RAZED THE HOUSE AT THE END OF THE BLOCK.

 OOPSIE!

GAH!

THIS TIME, THE FIREBREAK WORKED. THE BENTLEY WAS SAVED!

 YAY!

AND BECKY IS GOING TO JAIL.

AW.

BUT WAIT! I REALLY THOUGHT THAT DESTROYING THE HOUSE WASN'T AS BAD AS LOSING MY CAR!

IT DOESN'T MATTER.
WE DO CARE WHAT YOU BELIEVED
WHEN IT COMES TO THE IMMINENCE
OF DANGER, BUT WHEN IT COMES
TO THE LESSER OF TWO EVILS, THE
LAW WEIGHS THEM OBJECTIVELY.

AND SOMEONE'S HOUSE IS GONNA
OUTWEIGH YOUR CAR, NO MATTER
HOW NICE YOUR CAR MIGHT BE.

(ALSO, EVEN IF BECKY WAS PROTECTING
AN ORPHANAGE, THERE'S GOING TO
BE A QUESTION OF HOW IMMEDIATE
THE NEED WAS TO RAZE THE LAST
HOUSE ON THE BLOCK, FAR AWAY
FROM THE ACTUAL FIRE.

A JURY'S GOING TO HAVE
A HARD TIME BELIEVING THAT
BECKY ACTUALLY THOUGHT THE
DANGER WAS TRULY IMMINENT.)

JUST ONE LAST THING ABOUT NECESSITY:

JACK AND JILL WENT UP A CLIFF.

BUT JACKO WAS A DOPE.

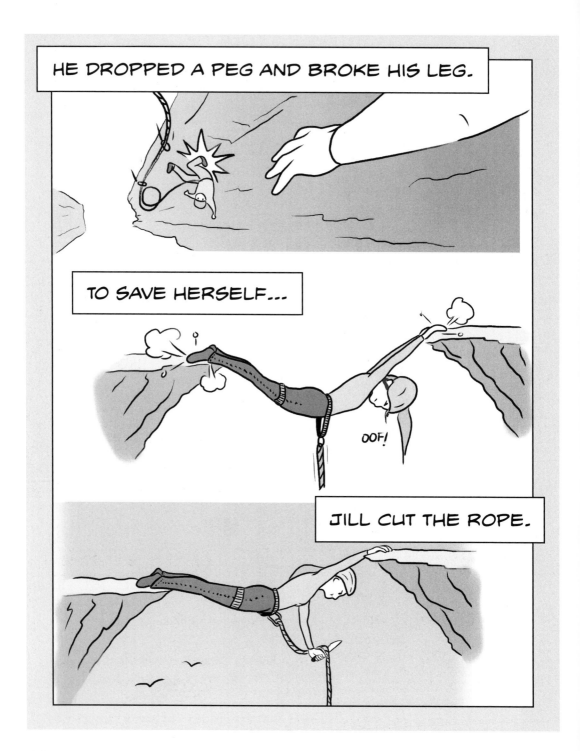

CAN JILL USE THE NECESSITY DEFENSE TO JUSTIFY KILLING JACK?

THIS JILL WASN'T GONNA COME TUMBLING AFTER!

IN MOST STATES, THE ANSWER IS A FLAT *NO*.

BETTER TO DIE THAN KILL AN INNOCENT.

UNLESS IT'S SELF-DEFENSE (WHICH IS DIFFERENT FROM NECESSITY), IT'S NEVER GOING TO BE OKAY.

EVEN IF TAKING ONE LIFE WOULD SAVE MANY OTHERS, THE TRADITIONAL VIEW HAS LONG BEEN THAT KILLING *ONE* INNOCENT PERSON IS THE *GREATER* HARM.

IN THIS CHAPTER, WHENEVER YOU SEE THOSE SCALES, YOU'RE MAKING AN OBJECTIVE MEASUREMENT. IT'S A STRICTLY UTILITARIAN EXERCISE.

BUT SOMETIMES THE STATE PUTS HER THUMB ON ONE OF THE SCALES. YOU'LL KNOW WHEN THAT HAPPENS, BECAUSE YOU'LL SEE PHRASES LIKE "AS A MATTER OF LAW."

SO IN MOST STATES, AS A MATTER OF LAW, KILLING AN INNOCENT PERSON TO SAVE OTHER LIVES IS NEVER THE LESSER OF TWO EVILS.

JILL COULD BE LOOKING AT JAIL.

A MINORITY OF STATES HAVE STARTED TO USE A MORE MODERN APPROACH, WHERE NECESSITY WOULD KNOCK JILL'S INTENTIONAL HOMICIDE DOWN TO A LESSER CHARGE, OR EVEN MAKE IT NO CRIME AT ALL.

BUT EVEN IN THOSE STATES, JILL MIGHT NOT GET OFF.

 HOW COME?

BECAUSE EVEN THERE THE HARM PREVENTED MUST BE **GREATER** THAN THE HARM DONE.

AND JACK'S LIFE WEIGHS THE **SAME** AS JILL'S LIFE.

SO THE QUESTION IS WHETHER JACK WAS GOING TO DIE ANYWAY. IF JACK WAS A GONER, THEN JILL ACTED SO THAT ONLY ONE WOULD DIE INSTEAD OF TWO. HER CHOICE OF EVILS WAS THIS:

DO NOTHING, AND **BOTH** DIE OR...

KILL **ONE**, SO THAT ONE **LIVES**.

IF JACK WAS GOING TO DIE ANYWAY, THEN UNDER THE MINORITY (MODERN) VIEW, BY KILLING HIM TO SAVE HERSELF, JILL DID THE **RIGHT THING**:

SHE CHOSE **ONE** DEATH INSTEAD OF **TWO**.

BUT IF JACK COULD HAVE SECURED HIMSELF? IF HIS DEATH WASN'T A FOREGONE CONCLUSION?

HOLD ON FOR A FEW MORE SECONDS, JILL, AND THEN YOU CAN LET GO!

THE HECK IS SHE DOING?

THEN IT **WASN'T** A CASE OF ONE DYING INSTEAD OF TWO.

IT WAS **ME** LIVING INSTEAD OF **YOU.**

ONE LIFE DOESN'T OUTWEIGH ANOTHER. TRADING ONE HARM FOR AN EQUAL HARM DOESN'T SERVE THE GREATER GOOD. IT'S AN **EQUIVALENT** EVIL, NOT THE LESSER EVIL.

IN STATES THAT JUSTIFY KILLING BY NECESSITY, IT'S MORE LIKELY TO WORK WHEN **SEVERAL** OTHER LIVES WERE SAVED BY TAKING THAT ONE LIFE.

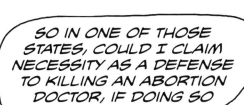

SO IN ONE OF THOSE STATES, COULD I CLAIM NECESSITY AS A DEFENSE TO KILLING AN ABORTION DOCTOR, IF DOING SO SAVES MANY —

I SEE WHERE YOU'RE GOING WITH THAT. THE ANSWER IS NO, BECAUSE ABORTION IS SPECIFICALLY PERMITTED BY THE STATE. AS A MATTER OF LAW, IT'S NOT A "HARM" AT ALL. SO IT JUST DOESN'T OUTBALANCE THE VALUE OF THE DOCTOR'S OWN LIFE.

AND ANYWAY, YOU'RE ONLY DOING IT TO PREVENT POSSIBLE FUTURE ACTS, NOT AN IMMEDIATE ACT GOING ON RIGHT NOW. THAT'S NEVER NECESSITY.

FOR THAT MATTER, THE NECESSITY DEFENSE DOESN'T JUSTIFY **ANY** CRIME THAT'S COMMITTED IN THE CAUSE OF CIVIL DISOBEDIENCE.

BREAKING **ONE** LAW TO PROTEST **ANOTHER** IS NOT NECESSARY. YOU CAN DO LAWFUL THINGS LIKE PETITION, MARCH, VOTE, LOBBY, ADVERTISE, ETC., TO CHANGE PUBLIC POLICY.

AND NOW, FINALLY, WE CAN MOVE ON TO THE JUICY DEFENSES OF DURESS AND SELF-DEFENSE.

IT'S ABOUT TIME!

EXCEPT, OH, WOULD YOU LOOK AT THAT? WE'RE OUT OF TIME.

WHAT! NOT AGAIN!

OH, ALL RIGHT. LET'S GET ON WITH IT, THEN....

"HE MADE ME DO IT!"

MEET THE GOLDEN HORDE, A LOCAL "OUTLAW" MOTORCYCLE CLUB.

THEY LIVE FOR VIOLENCE, MAYHEM, AND STIMULATING INTELLECTUAL DEBATE.

EXPLAIN AGAIN WHY SCHRÖDINGER'S CAT IS NOT IN SUPERPOSITION?

BECAUSE THAT ONLY WORKS IN ISOLATION!

THE CAT'S ENVIRONMENT CONSTANTLY COLLAPSES THE CAT-BOX SYSTEM... DUMMY.

THEY FINANCE THIS EXTRAVAGANT LIFESTYLE WITH DRUG TRAFFICKING AND PROSTITUTION.

ODDLY ENOUGH, HOWEVER, THEY DON'T ALLOW WOMEN INTO THEIR CLUB.

SO AS YOU CAN IMAGINE, STAFFING OUR PROSTITUTION DIVISION CAN SOMETIMES BE A BIT OF A PROBLEM.

TO SOLVE A RECENT PERSONNEL DEFICIT, THE GOLDEN HORDE KIDNAPPED VICKY, WHO WAS HERE ON SPRING BREAK.

THEY BROUGHT HER TO THE CLUB'S BROTHEL...

...AND MADE IT VERY CLEAR THAT SHE COULD EITHER START SERVICING THE CLIENTELE, OR ELSE...

THAT? OH THAT'S JILL, YOUR PREDECESSOR.

SHE SAID "NO" THIS MORNING.

VICKY DECIDED TO STAY ALIVE.

FORTUNATELY, THE POLICE RAIDED THE PLACE A FEW DAYS LATER.

YAY!

UNFORTUNATELY, VICKY HAS NOW BEEN CHARGED WITH SEVERAL COUNTS OF PROSTITUTION.

DURESS IS A **COMPLETE DEFENSE.**
THAT MEANS, IF IT APPLIES, THEN YOU DIDN'T
COMMIT A CRIME AT ALL. IT'S NOT THAT YOU'RE
EXCUSED FOR DOING IT, BUT THAT THERE'S
NOTHING TO EXCUSE IN THE FIRST PLACE.

SO LET'S SEE IF THIS DEFENSE APPLIES TO VICKY.

AS WITH EVERYTHING ELSE IN CRIMINAL LAW, EACH STATE DEFINES IT DIFFERENTLY. BUT IN GENERAL:

FIRST: SOMEONE ELSE HAS TO HAVE MADE A *THREAT*—THAT YOU COMMIT THE CRIME OR ELSE.

EITHER YOU RENT OUT THAT HOLE, OR I GIVE YOU SOME NEW ONES.

SECOND: THE THREAT MUST GIVE AN ACTUAL *REASONABLE FEAR* (THAT YOU OR SOMEONE CLOSE TO YOU) WILL BE KILLED.

OR AT LEAST PRETTY SEVERELY INJURED.

THIRD: YOU MUST FEAR THAT IT WOULD *HAPPEN RIGHT NOW.*

NOT AT SOME VAGUE POINT OUT IN THE UNCERTAIN FUTURE.

AND FOURTH: YOU CAN HAVE **NO OTHER WAY OUT.**

IT REALLY IS A CASE OF "DO OR DIE."

DURESS IS A **COMPLETE DEFENSE** BECAUSE YOU'RE BEING FORCED TO DO IT AGAINST YOUR WILL.

THAT PRETTY MUCH DOES AWAY WITH THE WHOLE "MENS REA" THING.

AND THUS, THE WHOLE "CRIME" THING, REALLY.

IN THIS CASE, THE GOLDEN HORDE THREATENED TO KILL VICKY THEN AND THERE IF SHE DIDN'T COMMIT PROSTITUTION FOR THEM.

SHE WAS IN PERFECTLY REASONABLE FEAR FOR HER LIFE, AND COULD NOT HAVE ESCAPED.

SO YES, VICKY CAN ASSERT THE DEFENSE OF DURESS. SHE MAY HAVE COMMITTED THE ACT, BUT SHE COMMITTED NO CRIME.

DIDN'T I JUST **SAY** THAT?

BUT WHAT ABOUT STU, HERE?

Y'KNOW, IS THIS REALLY ETHICAL?

IT DEPENDS ON WHAT YOU MEAN BY "ETHICAL."

THE GOLDEN HORDE KIDNAPPED HIM, TOO, BUT TO FILL *DIFFERENT* PERSONNEL REQUIREMENTS.

IT SEEMS THAT SNITCHY McSNITCHERSON RATTED OUT ONE HORDE BROTHER TOO MANY, AND THEY WANT HIM DEAD.

WELL, **WE** BELIEVE IT IS RIGHT AND JUST THAT SNITCHY MUST DIE.

BUT THE **LAW** SAYS IT'S WRONG, AND WOULD PUNISH US FOR KILLING HIM.

RIGHT, WHICH IS WHY STU HERE IS GOING TO SHOOT HIM **FOR** US.

BUT THAT'S WHAT I'M SAYING: IS IT RIGHT TO MAKE SOMEONE ELSE ENFORCE OUR MORALITY?

DRUG TRAFFICKING IS PROBABLY THE HORDE'S MOST PROFITABLE ENTERPRISE. ONE OF THEIR BEST WORKERS FOR A LONG TIME WAS MILLIE THE MULE.

SHE HAULED ALL KINDS OF POWDERS FOR YEARS, WITHOUT EVER BEING STOPPED.

YEAH, CUZ I LOOK ALL INNOCENT AND STUFF.

BUT A FEW MONTHS AGO, SHE GOT ARRESTED. THE D.A. MADE HER A DEAL, AND NOW MILLIE IS GETTING READY TO **TESTIFY** AGAINST THE HORDE AT A BIG TRIAL.

I CLEAN UP GOOD, HUH?

BEFORE SHE TAKES THE STAND, ONE OF THE HORDE MEMBERS MAKES A SIMPLE **THREAT:**

*IF YOU TELL THE TRUTH, THEN WE'LL HUNT YOU DOWN AND KILL YOU WHEN YOU LEAST **EXPECT** IT.*

IT'S A SERIOUS THREAT, AND MILLIE TAKES IT SERIOUSLY. WHEN SHE TAKES THE STAND, SHE LIES UNDER OATH.

GOLDEN HORDE? NEVER HEARD OF 'EM.

NEEDLESS TO SAY, THE PROSECUTOR WAS DISPLEASED. MILLIE IS NOW BEING CHARGED WITH **PERJURY.**

BUT I DID IT UNDER DURESS!

UNFORTUNATELY FOR MILLIE, IN MOST STATES THAT **WASN'T** ENOUGH TO MAKE IT DURESS.

IN MOST JURISDICTIONS, YOU HAVE TO BE AFRAID OF BEING HURT **IMMEDIATELY,** NOT AT SOME POINT IN THE FUTURE.

SOME STATES GIVE YOU A LITTLE MORE WIGGLE ROOM, AS LONG AS THE THREAT WAS ENOUGH TO OVERCOME A REASONABLE PERSON'S FREE WILL.

BUT EVEN IN THOSE STATES, MILLIE MIGHT HAVE A PROBLEM HERE, BECAUSE THE THREAT WAS SO *UNCERTAIN.*

"ONE OF THESE DAYS" ISN'T QUITE AS **INTIMIDATING** AS "RIGHT AFTER THE TRIAL."

IT'S A MATTER OF DEGREE, SO IT MAY HAVE TO BE UP TO A JURY TO DECIDE.

AND MILLIE'S ISN'T ONE OF THOSE STATES, SO NOW SHE'S LOOKING AT *JAIL* TIME FOR LYING UNDER OATH.

OH, AND FOR HER ORIGINAL DRUG CHARGES, AS WELL.

SHE KIND OF **VIOLATED** THE TERMS OF HER COOPERATION AGREEMENT WITH THE STATE.

WHAT WITH THE PROSTITUTION RAID AND THE DRUG BUSTS, THE HORDE IS STARTING TO RUN LOW ON CASH. TO RAISE CAPITAL, THEY'RE TURNING TO **BANK ROBBERY.**

THEY KIDNAPPED BOB AND JIM TO DO THE ACTUAL ROBBERIES.

BOB'S FREE WILL WAS PRETTY EASY TO OVERCOME.

EITHER YOU ROB THAT BANK OR WE'RE GONNA **KILL** YOUR LITTLE **GIRL.**

HERE'S A PHOTO OF HER AT OUR CLUBHOUSE, TO PROVE THAT WE ARE **SERIOUS.**

BOB DID AS HE WAS TOLD, TRIED TO ROB THE FIRST NATIONAL BANK, AND WAS IMMEDIATELY **ARRESTED** BY THE LOCAL SWAT TEAM.

ACROSS THE STATE, JIM WAS ALSO THREATENED...

SEE THE LITTLE GIRL IN THIS PHOTO. YOU **DON'T KNOW** HER, BUT WE'RE GONNA KILL HER IF YOU DON'T ROB THAT BANK RIGHT NOW.

SO WHAT IF HE DIDN'T KNOW HER? THREATENING THAT LITTLE GIRL'S LIFE WAS **ENOUGH** TO OVERCOME JIM'S WILL, AS WELL.

THE COPS GOT HIM, TOO.

BOB SUCCESSFULLY CLAIMED **DURESS**, AND WENT FREE.

MOST STATES RECOGNIZE THE DEFENSE WHEN SOMEONE IN YOUR IMMEDIATE **FAMILY** IS THE ONE BEING THREATENED.

IT DOESN'T HAVE TO BE YOUR **OWN** SKIN YOU'RE PROTECTING.

BUT BELIEVE IT OR NOT, JIM IS PROBABLY GOING TO JAIL.

YOU'RE KIDDING ME.

SOME STATES **HAVE** BEEN STARTING TO ALLOW A DEFENSE OF DURESS WHEN THE THREAT WAS AGAINST A STRANGER, BUT EVEN THERE JIM MIGHT HAVE A PROBLEM.

BASICALLY, THE MORE **DISTANT** THE RELATIONSHIP, THE **LESS** LIKELY THE LAW WILL ACCEPT THAT A REASONABLE PERSON WOULD HAVE BEEN "UNABLE TO RESIST."

THAT'S FREAKIN' STUPID.

NOT REALLY. AMERICAN LAW DOESN'T RECOGNIZE A **DUTY** TO PROTECT STRANGERS, AND AS THIS IS ALL ABOUT COMPETING DUTIES (TO THE LAW AND TO OTHERS)...

I DISAGREE. IT'S SIMPLY A QUESTION OF THE LAW FAILING TO KEEP UP WITH EVOLVING SOCIETAL NORMS.

I CONCUR.

MODERN SENSIBILITIES ARE MORE LIKELY TO FEEL PROTECTIVE OF OTHERS BEYOND ONE'S IMMEDIATE FAMILY. ESPECIALLY CHILDREN.

PERHAPS, BUT THE LAW HASN'T CAUGHT UP TO THAT, YET.

THAT'S NO DIFFERENT FROM WHAT I WAS SAYING.

AND AS SOON AS THE LAW **DOES** CATCH UP, YOU CAN EXPECT THAT IT'LL IMPOSE AN OUTRIGHT DUTY TO PROTECT OTHERS, WHICH ISN'T THE CASE NOW.

SO IT MIGHT ACTUALLY BECOME A **CRIME** TO **NOT** HELP A STRANGER?

IT'D HAVE TO BE! JUST AS IT CAN BE CRIMINAL NOW TO FAIL TO PROTECT YOUR OWN KIDS.

DOES THE PROTECTION OF THE DURESS DEFENSE STEM FROM THIS DUTY TO PROTECT, OR IS IT THE OTHER WAY AROUND?

NO. THE DUTY AND THE DEFENSE ARE CO-EMERGENT, MERE ASPECTS OF THE SAME...

ENOUGH OF THAT!

THE POINT IS THAT JIM IS IN TROUBLE, EVEN THOUGH HE ALMOST CERTAINLY DID THE RIGHT THING.

IT'S NOT FAIR, BUT IT'S HOW THE LAW IS AT THE MOMENT.

(WHEN WE GET TO PROCEDURE, WE'LL SEE HOW PROSECUTORIAL DISCRETION AND THE GRAND JURY ARE SUPPOSED TO SMOOTH OUT SUCH WRINKLES, IN THEORY AT LEAST.)

FINALLY, LET'S MEET TROG, A PROSPECT WHO RECENTLY **JOINED UP** WITH THE HORDE.

IT JUST FEELS RIGHT.

TO PROVE HIMSELF **WORTHY** OF FULL MEMBERSHIP, HE MUST FIRST KIDNAP AND RAPE A RANDOM INNOCENT WOMAN, IN FRONT OF OTHER GANG MEMBERS.

I DON'T THINK SO, GUYS. THAT JUST FEELS WRONG!

TOO BAD! YOU CAN'T BACK OUT NOW. EITHER YOU PASS INITIATION...

OR WE PUT A BULLET IN YOUR BRAIN.

WELL, IF YOU PUT IT **THAT** WAY...

AND SO TROG, FEARING FOR HIS *LIFE*,
COMMITTED KIDNAPPING, RAPE,
AND A FEW OTHER CRIMES.

SO IT LOOKS LIKE TROG'S GOING TO JAIL, TOO.

YOU CAN'T PUT **YOURSELF** INTO A SITUATION WHERE YOU MIGHT BE PLACED UNDER DURESS, AND THEN EXPECT TO BE HELD **BLAMELESS** FOR THE CRIMES YOU THEN COMMIT AS A RESULT.

AAAAND THAT'S PRETTY MUCH IT FOR DURESS, REALLY.

YOU KNOW, NECESSITY AND DURESS ARE INTERESTING AND ALL, BUT THEY DON'T COME UP IN REAL LIFE AS OFTEN AS YOU MIGHT THINK.

SELF-DEFENSE, ON THE OTHER HAND, COMES UP **ALL THE TIME.**

AND IT CAN BE TRICKY, ESPECIALLY WHEN SOMEONE **KILLS** IN SELF-DEFENSE.

SO LET'S GET TO ALL OF THAT STUFF NOW...

"IT WAS EITHER HIM OR ME!"

RICO THE RUSTLER WAS RIDING THE RANGE LAST NIGHT, LOOKING FOR SOME CATTLE TO STEAL.

AT THEIR NEARBY RANCH, HOWEVER, THE MORGAN BROTHERS WERE READY AND WAITING FOR HIM.

YOU READY, EDDIE?

AND WAITING, ARNOLD.

THE INSTANT RICO ROPED ONE OF THEIR STEERS, EDDIE LEAPED INTO ACTION.

DROP IT OR YOU'RE DEAD!

BUT THEN ARNOLD DID SOMETHING *STRANGE.*

NO, BRO!

PUT THAT GUN AWAY!

THE HECK IS YOUR *PROBLEM*, ARNOLD?

YOU CAN'T USE *DEADLY FORCE...* TO PREVENT SOMEONE FROM STEALING MERE *PROPERTY!*

I CAN *THREATEN* TO SHOOT, CAN'T I?

IN SOME STATES, MAYBE. BUT YOU WERE *GONNA* SHOOT. (I KNOW YOU, ARNOLD.) AND YOU CAN *NEVER* KILL SOMEONE JUST TO STOP THEM FROM TAKING YOUR *STUFF.*

LATER THAT NIGHT...

ON THE WAY BACK HOME, ARNOLD RECOGNIZED A FEW MORE OF THE MORGAN BROTHERS' CATTLE ON RICO'S LAND.

RICO'S RANCH HANDS RAN OUT TO STOP THEM.

BUT THEN **RICO** DID SOMETHING STRANGE...

I DON'T WANT YOU BOYS GOING TO JAIL WITH ME.

BUT THEY'RE TAKING OUR CATTLE! CAN'T WE AT LEAST USE **NON**-DEADLY FORCE TO STOP THEM?

NO, BOYS. THEY'RE ONLY TAKING BACK THEIR **OWN** COWS, LAWFULLY.

YOU CAN ONLY USE FORCE IF THEY'RE DOING IT **UN**LAWFULLY.

DANG.

I HATE TO INTERRUPT THIS LITTLE DIGRESSION ON DEFENSE OF PROPERTY, BUT THIS HERE CHAPTER IS SUPPOSED TO BE ABOUT **SELF**-DEFENSE.

SO GET ON WITH IT... **PARDNER.**

VERY WELL, THEN. LET'S HEAD OVER TO TOWN...

...TO THE SALOON, WHERE THE MORGAN BROTHERS WENT THE NEXT DAY TO CELEBRATE THE RECAPTURE OF THEIR CATTLE.

OVER AT THE BAR, LAREDO LUKE WAS JUST MINDING HIS OWN BUSINESS.

ALONG CAME A COUPLE OF OUTLAWS.

WE DON'T LIKE YOU.

SORRY.

WATCH YOURSELF, BOY. WE'RE WANTED MEN.

I'LL BE CAREFUL.

YOU'LL BE...

WITH THE BARTENDER OFF SHERIFFING, BADLANDS BRITT SNUCK HIMSELF A MUG OF BEER.

HEY, YOU CAN'T DO THAT!

MIND YER OWN BUSINESS, PIPSQUEAK.

OH NO YOU DON'T!

ARNOLD HIT BRITT *FIRST*! AIN'T HE GONNA GET IN TROUBLE?

NAH, THAT WAS SELF-DEFENSE.

YOU **DON'T** HAVE TO **WAIT** FOR THE OTHER GUY TO HIT YOU FIRST.

SO LONG AS YOU REASONABLY BELIEVE THAT YOU'RE ABOUT TO GET HURT, YOU'RE ALLOWED TO HURT **FIRST** TO PREVENT IT FROM HAPPENING.

AND YOU'RE ALLOWED TO KEEP **ON** HITTING UNTIL THE OTHER GUY ISN'T A **THREAT** TO YOU ANYMORE.

I SEE BRITT'S FIGHTING BACK, NOW. DOES **THAT** COUNT AS SELF-DEFENSE?

NO, MA'AM. ARNOLD WAS HITTING HIM **LAWFULLY.** YOU CAN ONLY USE FORCE TO PROTECT YOURSELF AGAINST **UNLAWFUL** ATTACKS.

APOLOGIES TO MORT WALKER

THE SHERIFF AGREES WITH YOU. BRITT'S GETTING LOCKED UP FOR ASSAULT, IT LOOKS LIKE.

AND WITH THE SHERIFF AWAY, ANOTHER FIGHT SOON BROKE OUT.

 OKAY, SO FOR **NON-DEADLY** FORCE, YOU'RE ALLOWED TO **HURT** SOMEONE TO STOP OR PREVENT THEM FROM HURTING YOU, SO LONG AS...

...YOU DIDN'T **START** IT (THERE'S STILL NO CHUTZPAH DEFENSE)

...AND YOU DON'T USE ANY MORE FORCE THAN IS REASONABLY **NECESSARY** TO PROTECT YOURSELF.

(AS IT'S NOT A LAST RESORT, YOU **DON'T** HAVE TO TRY TO ESCAPE FIRST.)

 BUT **DEADLY** FORCE IS A BIT DIFFERENT. SO LET'S SEE HOW THAT WORKS NOW.

CALEB FIFER LEFT THE SALOON FAR MORE DRUNK THAN USUAL.

WHEN HE GOT HOME, HE FOUND THAT HE'D FORGOTTEN HIS KEYS.

SO HE CRAWLED IN THROUGH THE PARLOR WINDOW.

UNFORTUNATELY, IT WASN'T HIS OWN PARLOR WINDOW. THIS WAS RODEO ROWAN'S HOUSE.

CALEB WASN'T EVEN ON THE RIGHT STREET.

AS SOON AS ROWAN SAW CALEB CRAWLING THROUGH HIS WINDOW, HE GRABBED HIS SHOTGUN.

BLAM!

THE SHERIFF WAS THERE WITHIN MINUTES.

SO WAS CALEB'S FAMILY.

AFTER HEARING WHAT HAPPENED...

WELL, IT WAS A SAD ACCIDENT. BUT ROWAN SHOT IN SELF-DEFENSE, SO I'M NOT GONNA ARREST HIM.

WELL, HERE'S HOW IT WORKS...

WHAT!?

NO WAY. DEADLY FORCE CAN ONLY BE USED AS A **LAST** RESORT IN SELF-DEFENSE. RODEO ROWAN SHOT CALEB **FIRST**, NOT LAST!

MOST OF THE TIME, YOU'RE **NEVER** JUSTIFIED IN USING DEADLY FORCE, **UNLESS:**

1 YOU REASONABLY BELIEVE YOU'RE IN **IMMINENT DANGER** OF <u>DEATH</u>, <u>RAPE</u>, <u>KIDNAPPING</u>, OR SERIOUS BODILY <u>HARM</u>...

2 YOU REASONABLY BELIEVE THAT DEADLY FORCE IS **NECESSARY** TO PROTECT YOURSELF...

3 YOU DIDN'T PROVOKE THE THREAT **YOURSELF**... AND

4 YOU WEREN'T AWARE OF ANY COMPLETELY SAFE **RETREAT.**

FINE.

BUT HOW ON EARTH COULD ROWAN HAVE **BELIEVED** THAT CALEB WAS GOING TO HURT HIM?

HOME INVASIONS ARE OFTEN **VIOLENT.**

BUT WHAT MADE YOU THINK THAT **THIS** ONE WAS?

HANG ON. THE LAW **DOESN'T** REQUIRE YOU TO TAKE THE TIME TO FIND OUT WHAT AN INTRUDER'S **INTENTIONS** ARE.

AND I WASN'T TAKING THAT CHANCE.

ALSO, I CLEARLY DIDN'T PROVOKE THE THREAT. I DIDN'T **MAKE** HIM COME IN MY WINDOW. SO NUMBER 3 IS EASY.

BUT WHAT ABOUT NUMBER 4? YOU COULD HAVE JUST **LEFT** THE HOUSE! END OF THREAT!

AS A MATTER OF LAW IN THIS STATE, AS IN MOST STATES, ROWAN HAD **NO** DUTY TO RETREAT FROM HIS **OWN HOME.**

SOCIETY DOESN'T EXPECT YOU TO MAKE YOURSELF A **REFUGEE** FROM WHAT IS SUPPOSED TO BE YOUR ULTIMATE **REFUGE.**

THAT'S CONDITIONS 1, 3, AND 4. BUT WHAT ABOUT #2?

YEAH, HOW COULD HE HAVE REASONABLY BELIEVED THAT DEADLY FORCE WAS **NECESSARY** TO DEFUSE THE THREAT?

WHAT, YOU WANT ME TO RISK MY FAMILY GETTING **SHOT** BY SOME...

BUT YOU'RE RODEO ROWAN! **FASTEST LASSO** IN THE WEST! YOU COULDA HAD HIM ROPED AND TIED BEFORE HE WAS THROUGH THE WINDOW!

BUT I...

SAY, THAT'S **RIGHT.** AND YOUR LARIAT WAS RIGHT THERE, TOO.

I THINK YOU'D BETTER COME WITH ME, ROWAN.

YOU'RE CHARGING ME WITH MURDER?

NO, NOT MURDER.

WHEN YOU THINK YOU'RE ACTING IN SELF-DEFENSE, BUT YOU WERE WRONG ABOUT ONE OF THE FOUR REQUIREMENTS, YOU HAVE WHAT'S CALLED "IMPERFECT SELF-DEFENSE."

IT GETS YOU A LESSER MANSLAUGHTER CHARGE, INSTEAD.

AND IF I HADN'T BEEN THE FASTEST LASSO...?

YOU'D PROBABLY HAVE BEEN JUSTIFIED IN USING DEADLY FORCE TO DEFEND YOURSELF AND YOUR FAMILY.

IN **SOME** STATES, SO LONG AS YOU'RE IN YOUR HOME, YOU CAN USE DEADLY FORCE AGAINST AN UNLAWFUL INTRUDER WHEN YOU REASONABLY BELIEVE HE IS GOING TO USE EVEN THE **SLIGHTEST** AMOUNT OF FORCE AGAINST ANYONE INSIDE THE HOUSE.

SUCH "MAKE MY DAY" LAWS ONLY **MODIFY** THE RULES FOR DEADLY FORCE. THEY DO **NOT** GIVE YOU CARTE BLANCHE TO START SHOOTING AT TRESPASSERS.

THAT'S A BAD MYTH.

 JOHNNY WAS JUSTIFIED IN SHOOTING **FIRST**. JUST AS WITH NON-DEADLY FORCE, YOU **DON'T** HAVE TO **WAIT** FOR THE OTHER GUY TO START SHOOTING AT YOU BEFORE YOU'RE ALLOWED TO PROTECT YOURSELF.

JOHNNY REASONABLY BELIEVED THAT HE WAS ABOUT TO BE SHOT, AND THAT DEADLY FORCE WAS NECESSARY. HE DIDN'T CREATE THE SITUATION IN THE FIRST PLACE, AND HE DIDN'T HAVE ANY PERFECTLY SAFE RETREAT.

HE **LAWFULLY** USED DEADLY FORCE IN SELF-DEFENSE.

BUT WHAT IF HE COULD HAVE **RETREATED** SAFELY?

OUTSIDE HIS HOME OR WORKPLACE, HE'D HAVE A **DUTY** IN MOST STATES TO **RETREAT** BEFORE USING DEADLY FORCE.

(SOME STATES HAVE WHAT'S KNOWN AS A "STAND YOUR GROUND" LAW, WHICH BASICALLY ELIMINATES THE DUTY TO RETREAT... **IF** YOU WERE ALREADY ENTITLED TO BE WHERE THE ATTACK OCCURRED.)

ALSO, "STAND YOUR GROUND" LAWS ONLY PERMIT YOU TO USE **JUST ENOUGH** FORCE TO REPEL AN ATTACK. AND THEY CERTAINLY DON'T GIVE YOU CARTE BLANCHE TO START SHOOTING PEOPLE YOU FEEL THREATENED BY.

(APART FROM BEING WIDELY MISUNDERSTOOD, THE "MAKE MY DAY" AND "STAND YOUR GROUND" LAWS ARE NOT TECHNICALLY DEFENSES, BUT INSTEAD PROVIDE AN IMMUNITY FROM PROSECUTION IN THE FIRST PLACE. BUT THAT'S NOT IMPORTANT FOR OUR PURPOSES HERE.)

MEANWHILE...

JUDGE BAHR HAD JUST HELD UP THE BANK, AND WAS MAKING HIS GETAWAY.

I'LL GET HIM, FELLAS.

NOT IF I GET YOU **FIRST**!

THE SHERIFF ARRESTED BAHR FOR *MURDER*, AS WELL AS ARMED ROBBERY.

BUT HE WAS GONNA **SHOOT** ME! IT WAS SELF-DEFENSE!

YOU KNOW BETTER THAN THAT, JUDGE. YOU CAN'T CLAIM SELF-DEFENSE IF YOU **CREATED** THE SITUATION.

HELP! HELP! THERE'S BEEN A TERRIBLE ACCIDENT!

INSIDE THE BANK...

WHEN BAHR WAS SHOOTING AT ME, I SHOT BACK. BUT I MISSED, AND HIT POOR LI'L **IVY** INSTEAD!

I DIDN'T KNOW SHE WAS THERE!

IT'S A SAD ACCIDENT, BUT YOU DIDN'T COMMIT A CRIME.

JUST LIKE YOUR HOME, YOU DON'T HAVE TO RETREAT FROM YOUR PLACE OF BUSINESS. AND YOU WERE JUSTIFIED IN USING DEADLY FORCE TO PROTECT YOURSELF.

BUT IVY?

WELL, BY SHOOTING YOUR GUN IN THE BANK, YOU CREATED A SUBSTANTIAL RISK TO INNOCENT BYSTANDERS. HOWEVER, THE LAW WILL USUALLY **LET** YOU CREATE SOME PRETTY SUBSTANTIAL RISKS IN ORDER TO SAVE YOUR OWN **LIFE**.

SAY WHAT?

IN THOSE SITUATIONS WHERE DEADLY FORCE WAS ALREADY JUSTIFIED, OF COURSE.

IF YOU WERE JUST SHOOTING WILD, THAT'D PROBABLY HAVE BEEN TOO **RECKLESS**, AND I'D BE TAKING YOU IN FOR MANSLAUGHTER. BUT IN THIS CASE, IT WAS JUST A TRAGIC **ACCIDENT** ON YOUR PART.

*BAHR WILL GET CHARGED WITH IVY'S DEATH, OF COURSE, AS A FELONY MURDER.

LATER...

AS NIGHT FELL, EDDIE DECIDED IT WAS TIME TO HEAD HOME.

HE HEARD SCREAMS.

AT THE END OF THE ALLEY, EDDIE SAW AN OUTLAW TRYING TO RAPE A WOMAN.

SHE COULDN'T ESCAPE, AND IT WAS PRETTY CLEAR THAT SHE'D HAVE BEEN JUSTIFIED IN USING DEADLY FORCE TO PROTECT HERSELF.

SO EDDIE DID IT **FOR** HER.

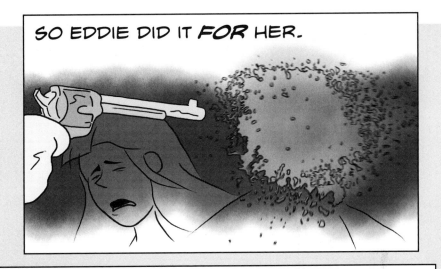

HIS ACT WAS JUSTIFIED, BECAUSE WHEN USING FORCE TO PROTECT SOMEONE **ELSE**, YOU'RE ALLOWED TO TAKE THE SAME ACTIONS THAT **THEY** COULD HAVE TAKEN.

SO EVEN THOUGH **EDDIE** COULD HAVE SAFELY GONE TO GET HELP, HE HAD NO DUTY TO RETREAT BECAUSE **SHE** COULDN'T HAVE DONE SO SAFELY.

IN MOST STATES, WHAT'S IMPORTANT ISN'T SO MUCH THE ACTUAL FACTS, BUT WHAT EDDIE REASONABLY **BELIEVED** THE FACTS TO BE.

STILL, IN REAL LIFE, IT'S BEST TO MAKE DARN SURE YOU **KNOW** WHAT'S GOING ON BEFORE USING FORCE TO DEFEND A STRANGER.

BACK AT THE SALOON, AFTER LAST CALL...

AT HOME, LILLIE FOUND HER HUSBAND **HANK**...

WHAT TOOK YOU SO LONG?

DRUNK AS USUAL.

TWO YEARS OF THIS. IT'S ONLY GETTING **WORSE.**

IF THIS GOES ON MUCH LONGER, HE'S GOING TO **KILL** ME.

HE'S **GOING** TO KILL ME.

WHEN LILLIE DIDN'T SHOW UP FOR WORK THAT DAY, THE SHERIFF CAME BY TO SEE WHAT WAS UP.

MY GOD, LILLIE, WHAT HAVE YOU DONE?

AFTER TELLING HIM THE TRUTH ABOUT WHAT HAPPENED...

SO YOU SEE, SHERIFF, I JUST **HAD** TO DO IT. IT WAS **SELF-DEFENSE!**

OH LILLIE, NO.

THAT'S **NOT** HOW IT WORKS, LILLIE. YOU HAD TO BELIEVE HE WAS GOING TO KILL YOU **RIGHT NOW.**

NOT AT SOME POINT IN THE FUTURE.

AND **NO** REASONABLE PERSON WOULD HAVE THOUGHT YOU WERE IN IMMINENT DANGER WHILE HE WAS **ASLEEP**.

BUT ALL THOSE BEATINGS...

LILLIE... MAYBE HE NEEDED KILLIN'. BUT EVEN IN **THIS** STATE THERE'S NO "HE NEEDED KILLIN'" DEFENSE.

A HISTORY OF ABUSE IS USEFUL TO SHOW THE **REASONABLENESS** OF A BATTERED WOMAN'S BELIEF THAT SHE'S **ABOUT** TO BE KILLED, BUT THAT'S AS FAR AS IT GOES.

BUT WHAT **ELSE** COULD I HAVE DONE? YOU WANT ME TO RUN AWAY AND BE A **FUGITIVE** FROM MY OWN HOME?

WHY NOT GET A COURT ORDER AND KICK **HIM** OUT? YOU HAD **OTHER OPTIONS**.

AND THAT'S SELF-DEFENSE IN A NUTSHELL.

AS WITH THE OTHER JUSTIFICATION DEFENSES, A VALID SELF-DEFENSE CLAIM MEANS YOU DID **THE RIGHT THING.** IT MAY BE SAD OR UNPLEASANT, BUT YOU DID NOTHING WRONG, AND SOCIETY DOESN'T WANT TO PUNISH YOU.

AND THAT ALSO WRAPS UP OUR DISCUSSION OF DEFENSES IN GENERAL.

BEFORE WE START TALKING ABOUT SOME DIFFERENT TYPES OF CRIMES, AND THEIR ELEMENTS, LET'S FIRST TAKE A LOOK AT WHERE THE LAW COMES FROM...

...AS WELL AS THAT ODD CREATION, THE "STRICT LIABILITY" CRIME, WHICH DOESN'T REQUIRE ANY CULPABLE **MENS REA.**

SO LET'S GET TO IT!

"PROBLEMS AND SOLUTIONS"

GUILT WITHOUT FAULT

TRUDY WAS JUST SUNBATHING IN HER BACKYARD LAST WEEK, WHEN...

IT WAS JUST AN ORDINARY SPARROW FEATHER, BUT TO TRUDY IT WAS SPECIAL.

SHE PUT IT WITH THE OTHERS IN HER COLLECTION:

A HAWK FEATHER SHE'D FOUND IN THE PARK,

A CROW FEATHER FROM HER UNCLE'S CORNFIELD,

AND A SEAGULL FEATHER FROM HER FIRST KISS.

WHILE TELLING A GIRLFRIEND ABOUT HER FEATHERS THE NEXT DAY, SHE WAS... OVERHEARD.

THIS MORNING, SPECIAL AGENTS FROM THE U.S. FISH & WILDLIFE SERVICE CAME WITH A SPECIAL WARRANT.

TRUDY WAS ARRESTED, AND CHARGED WITH FOUR VIOLATIONS OF THE MIGRATORY BIRD TREATY ACT.

(WHICH, AMONG OTHER THINGS, FORBIDS THE POSSESSION OF ANY PART, INCLUDING FEATHERS, OF MOST BIRDS ONE MIGHT FIND IN THE WILD... ALIVE OR NOT.)

NOW SHE'S LOOKING AT UP TO SIX MONTHS IN FEDERAL PRISON... FOR EACH FEATHER!

THAT'S NOT **FAIR!**

IT'S THE LAW.

BUT HOW COULD I HAVE **KNOWN** IT WAS A CRIME?

IGNORANCE OF THE LAW IS STILL NO EXCUSE.

BUT COLLECTING **FEATHERS?** OF BIRDS THAT AREN'T EVEN ENDANGERED?

CRIME IS WHEN YOU DO SOMETHING BAD!

WHERE'S THE **HARM** IN PICKING UP FEATHERS?

HARM'S GOT NOTHING TO DO WITH IT. IT'S A CRIME BECAUSE THE LAW **SAYS** SO.

NOW HOLD STILL....

DENNIS RUNS A COMPANY IN KANSAS THAT MAKES TURTLE SOUP.

HIS MAIN INGREDIENT, THE COMMON SNAPPING TURTLE, THRIVES ALL OVER THE CONTINENT, SO HE HAS MANY SUPPLIERS.

THEY DON'T CALL US "COMMON" FOR NOTHIN'!

RECENTLY, SCHOOLCHILDREN IN NEW YORK CHOSE THE SNAPPING TURTLE AS THE OFFICIAL STATE REPTILE, MAKING IT A PROTECTED SPECIES IN THAT STATE.

DID YOU KNOW THIS? NEITHER DID DENNIS.

AND HE COULDN'T HAVE KNOWN THAT ONE OF HIS SUPPLIERS WAS SHIPPING TURTLES THAT HAD COME FROM NEW YORK.

THE FEDS FOUND OUT, THOUGH.

FREEDOM!

NY ♡ TURTLES LIVE
NY ♡ TURTLES LIVE
NY ♡ TURTLES LIVE

SO NOW DENNIS IS UNDER INDICTMENT FOR VIOLATING THE LACEY ACT — WHICH MAKES IT A CRIME TO BUY OR RECEIVE A SPECIES IN VIOLATION OF ANY STATE'S LAW.

OR EVEN THE LAW OF ANY OTHER COUNTRY!

DO YOU KNOW THE LAWS OF EVERY STATE AND COUNTRY?

HE'S LOOKING AT A YEAR IN PRISON FOR EACH CHARGE.

YOU'RE KIDDING. I'M FACING PRISON FOR NOT KNOWING EVERY RANDOM, UNFORESEEABLE LAW IN THE **WORLD**?

WHAT PART OF "IGNORANCE OF THE LAW IS NO EXCUSE" DON'T YOU PEOPLE UNDERSTAND?

BUT I HAD NO WAY OF **KNOWING** THAT THESE TURTLES HAD COME FROM NEW YORK!

WHAT ABOUT **MENS REA**?

SORRY, BUT THIS LAW **DOESN'T INCLUDE** ANY MENS REA ELEMENT.

BUT THAT'S NOT HOW IT'S SUPPOSED TO **WORK**. YOU **CAN'T** PUNISH ME IF I DIDN'T HAVE A CULPABLE STATE OF MIND!

SURE I CAN. IT'S A **"STRICT LIABILITY"** CRIME. THAT MEANS I GET TO PUNISH YOU JUST BECAUSE IT **HAPPENED**, EVEN IF IT WAS THE PUREST ACCIDENT.

NOW HOLD STILL....

IT'S NOT FAIR!

WE DIDN'T DO ANYTHING WRONG, WE HAD NO BAD MENS REA, AND WE HAD NO NOTICE THAT WE COULD GET IN TROUBLE!

WHAT THE HECK IS GOING ON HERE?

TRUDY AND DENNIS ARE VICTIMS OF A GROWING TREND IN AMERICAN CRIMINAL LAW CALLED *"OVERCRIMINALIZATION."*

HERE ARE THE MAIN SYMPTOMS:

1. THE BODY OF CRIMINAL LAWS HAS BECOME *INNUMERABLE.*

THE NUMBER OF CRIMES USED TO BE FAIRLY *MODEST.* AFTER ALL, FOR THE MOST PART, CRIMES WERE SIMPLY THOSE THINGS THAT EVERYONE *ALREADY UNDERSTOOD* TO BE DESERVING OF PUNISHMENT. HURTING PEOPLE, TAKING THEIR STUFF, EXTREME IMMORALITY, AND THE LIKE.

BUT THAT HASN'T BEEN THE CASE FOR A WHILE.

NOW THE NUMBER OF CRIMES IS QUITE LITERALLY *COUNTLESS* — EVERY ATTEMPT TO COUNT JUST THE FEDERAL CRIMES *ALONE* HAS FAILED.

(ESTIMATES RANGE AROUND 5,000 FEDERAL STATUTORY CRIMES, AND PERHAPS 300,000 REGULATORY ONES.)

PLUS EACH STATE AND CITY HAS ITS *OWN* EXPANDING SET OF CRIMINAL LAWS AND REGULATIONS.

2. WHAT IS ACTUALLY AGAINST THE LAW IS _UNKNOWABLE_.

IN OTHER WORDS, IT'S IMPOSSIBLE TO PREDICT WHAT KINDS OF THINGS COULD LAND YOU IN PRISON.

YOU'RE TELLING ME!

THE LAW IS UNKNOWABLE FOR SEVERAL REASONS: FOR ONE THING, THE _NUMBER_ OF CRIMES IS ITSELF UNKNOWABLE.

SO WHAT? YOU DON'T NEED TO READ EVERY LAW TO BE ABLE TO TELL RIGHT FROM WRONG.

EXCEPT THESE DAYS, IT'S NOT ALWAYS ABOUT RIGHT AND WRONG.

FOR EXAMPLE, LAWMAKERS FREQUENTLY MISS THE WHOLE POINT OF WHAT CRIMINAL LAW IS EVEN _FOR_.

LAWS ARE WRITTEN TOO BROADLY, AFFECTING PEOPLE WHO WERE NEVER _MEANT_ TO BE PUNISHED.

AND LAWS ARE WRITTEN SO VAGUELY, NOBODY CAN EVEN TELL WHAT THEY FORBID.

 MYSTERY CRIME

WHAT'S IN THE BOX?

 BACK UP A BIT. WHAT DID YOU MEAN, THAT LAWMAKERS ARE MISSING THE POINT?

CRIMINAL LAW IS THERE TO PUNISH BEHAVIOR THAT SOCIETY SEES AS SO BAD OR DANGEROUS THAT THE STATE NEEDS TO STEP IN AND HARM THE OFFENDER.

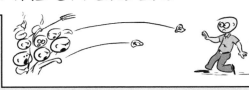

BUT NOW YOU SEE CRIMINAL PENALTIES IMPOSED, NOT FOR ANYTHING BAD, BUT FOR THINGS LIKE FAILING TO COMPLY WITH SOME ARBITRARY PROCEDURE...

 DO IT MY WAY!

DO IT MY WAY!

...OR AS A WAY TO FORCE SOCIETY TO CHANGE ITS WAYS.

REGULATORY AGENCIES, FOR EXAMPLE, COME UP WITH ZILLIONS OF PROCEDURES AND RULES FOR PEOPLE TO FOLLOW.

THESE ARE **CIVIL** RULES, NORMALLY ENFORCED WITH CIVIL PENALTIES.

FAIR ENOUGH. IF YOU'RE NOT GOING TO PLAY BY THEIR RULES, THEY DON'T HAVE TO LET YOU PLAY THEIR GAME. AND THERE ARE SOME REGULATIONS WHERE **CRIMINAL** PENALTIES CAN ALSO MAKE SENSE, SUCH AS THOSE PROTECTING PUBLIC SAFETY.

BUT NOWADAYS, REGULATORS ARE ADDING CRIMINAL PENALTIES TO RULES THAT HAVE NOTHING TO DO WITH PUBLIC SAFETY.

"Failure to file a Form K27 gets you one year in prison."

YEAH, BABY! NOW MY RULES HAVE **TEETH**!

THE REGS ARE WRITTEN BY GOVERNMENT WORKERS WHO AREN'T ELECTED, AND WITH ALMOST NO INPUT FROM THE COMMUNITY.

ARE YOU SAYING WE'RE OUT OF **TOUCH**?

I'LL HAVE YOU KNOW **NOBODY** UNDERSTANDS THIS POLICY BETTER!

THEY'RE EXPERTS, BUT IN THEIR OWN FIELD. THEY'RE **NOT** EXPERTS IN **CRIMINAL** LAW. SO THEY TEND TO LEAVE OUT IMPORTANT THINGS LIKE **MENS REA**.

MENZ **WHO**?

SIMILARLY, LAWMAKERS USE CRIMINAL LAW AS A WAY TO FORCE SOCIETY TO CHANGE, WHETHER IT WANTS TO OR NOT.

YOU'RE JAILING ME FOR NOT LIVING UP TO **YOUR** IDEALS?

YES! TO ENSURE PROGRESS, **NO** SACRIFICE IS TOO GREAT!

— IS THAT JEN THE ANARCHIST'S.... MOM?

WHEN LAWS PUNISH THINGS THAT FEW WOULD CONSIDER REALLY BAD, IT VIOLATES FUNDAMENTAL PRINCIPLES OF CRIMINAL LAW.

DID YOU JUST SAY I'M UNPRINCIPLED FOR HAVING **PRINCIPLES?**

NOT EXACTLY. SENATOR ERICSON, FOR EXAMPLE, HAS VERY **STRONG** PRINCIPLES.

NOBODY SHOULD BE ALLOWED TO DRIVE A **FOSSIL-FUEL** CAR!

OR DO... UH... **SEX STUFF** I DON'T LIKE!

THROUGH THE MAGIC OF THE LEGISLATIVE PROCESS, HE MANAGED TO STICK A PROVISION IN THE NEW JOBS BILL.

NOW IT'S A CRIME TO DRIVE A GAS-POWERED CAR!

MOST PEOPLE WOULDN'T **EXPECT** THIS TO BE AGAINST THE LAW, AND HE ALSO LEFT OUT ANY **MENS REA** ELEMENT.

SO HE MAY HAVE PRINCIPLES UP THE WAZOO, BUT HIS LAW **ITSELF** IS UNPRINCIPLED.

I DON'T CARE! DO IT MY WAY!

ALL OF THIS REFLECTS A FUNDAMENTAL SHIFT IN WHAT CRIMINAL LAW IS...

THE LAW STOPPED **DESCRIBING** WHAT SOCIETY'S VALUES **ARE**,

AND STARTED **PRESCRIBING** HOW SOMEONE THINKS THEY **OUGHT** TO BE.

AND THAT'S ONE WAY THE LAW BECAME UNKNOWABLE.

OKAY, THAT'S THE "MISSING THE POINT" PART, BUT YOU ALSO MENTIONED LAWS BEING "**OVERBROAD**?"

THAT'S RIGHT. SOMETIMES A LAW IS PASSED TO DEAL WITH A UNIQUE PROBLEM...

...BUT THEN THE LAW WINDS UP PUNISHING MORE PEOPLE THAN IT WAS REALLY **MEANT** TO.

GAH! IT'S A SWEEPING REFORM!

YOU GET THIS SLOPPINESS WHEN LAWS ARE RUSHED THROUGH (OFTEN IN THE HEAT OF PASSION AFTER A NOTORIOUS CASE) WITHOUT ANYONE TAKING MUCH TIME TO **THINK.**

THAT WAS A HORRIBLE CRIME!

WE PROMISE TO OVERREACT! PLEASE REELECT US!

AND SO, AFTER A SCHOOL SHOOTING, YOU
SEE KIDS GETTING ARRESTED FOR HAVING
A BUTTER KNIFE AT SCHOOL.

I DIDN'T EVEN KNOW
MY MOM HAD LEFT
IT THERE!

TOO BAD, KID.
ZERO TOLERANCE
MEANS STRICT
LIABILITY.

THINK OF
THE CHILDREN!

OR, IN RESPONSE TO A HORRIFIC SEX CRIME,
YOU FIND FOLKS GETTING PUNISHED AS SEX
OFFENDERS FOR SUCH UNRELATED THINGS
AS URINATING OUTSIDE.

MY LIFE IS RUINED
BECAUSE I TOOK
A **LEAK**?

YES!
THINK
OF THE
CHILDREN!

YOU CAN SOMETIMES SPOT THESE LAWS WHEN
THEY'RE NAMED AFTER A HIGH-PROFILE VICTIM.

SHOULDN'T THIS BE MORE
SPECIFIC? AND WHERE
IS THE MENS REA?

GASP!
THINK OF THE
CHILDREN!

YOU WANT ME TO **TRUST** THAT YOU WON'T BE TRYING TO GET YOUR NAME IN THE **PAPERS**? THAT YOU WON'T BE **PREJUDICED**? THAT YOU WON'T BE **STUPID**? THAT YOU WON'T BE A **JERK**?

YUP!

LADY JUSTICE HERE, AGAIN.

LOOK, FOR CRIMINAL LAW TO BE FAIR, IT HAS TO BE SOMEWHAT **PREDICTABLE**.

BUT WHEN CRIMES ARE TOO **NUMEROUS** TO COUNT...

WHEN YOU'RE PUNISHED NOT BECAUSE WHAT YOU DID WAS WRONG, BUT SIMPLY BECAUSE THE LAW **SAYS** SO...

WHEN LAWS ARE TOO **VAGUE** OR **OVERBROAD**...

THEN THE LAW **STOPS** BEING PREDICTABLE.

IT'S NOT **FAIR**!

AND THAT'S **NOT** JUSTICE.

BELIEVE IT OR NOT, THOUGH, THIS "OVERCRIMINALIZATION" IS **NOTHING NEW.** IT'S HAPPENED THROUGHOUT HISTORY.

IRONICALLY, IT'S WHAT HAPPENS AS THE LAW BECOMES MORE **CIVILIZED.**

SO BETTER JUSTICE CAUSES... INJUSTICE?

THAT **CAN'T** BE RIGHT.

HERE'S THE GENERAL PATTERN:

CRIMINAL LAW STARTS OUT SIMPLE, OFTEN LITTLE MORE THAN **CUSTOM** AND **TRADITION.**

EVERYONE KNOWS THE LAW, AND THE LAW REFLECTS THE COMMUNITY.

THIS SEEMS LIKE A **GOOD** THING.

BUT REALLY, IT KINDA **STINKS.**

FOR ONE THING, PEOPLE TEND TO TAKE THE LAW INTO THEIR **OWN HANDS.** ONLY RARELY WILL THE STATE GET INVOLVED.

I GOT THIS.

THE FIRST STEP TOWARDS CIVILIZATION IS WHEN THE STATE GAINS A **MONOPOLY** ON VIOLENCE AND PUNISHMENT.

NO, *I* GOT THIS.

THIS IS A **GOOD** THING.

AS LAW MAKES LIFE MORE **PREDICTABLE**, SOCIETY IS FREE AT LAST TO EVOLVE AND GROW MORE **COMPLEX.**

GOVERNMENT RESPONDS BY **SPECIALIZING**, AND ITSELF GROWING MORE COMPLEX TO MEET THE NEEDS OF SOCIETY.

THIS IS ALSO A **GOOD** THING.

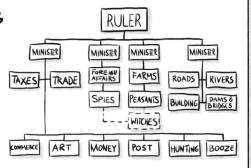

AS **SOME** PEOPLE GET MORE SAY IN GOVERNMENT, LAWMAKERS PAY MORE **ATTENTION** TO WHAT THE PEOPLE WANT.

THIS, TOO, IS A **GOOD** THING.

(FUNNY HATS ARE OPTIONAL.)

BUT A COMPLEX GOVERNMENT IS GOING TO NEED A LOT OF LAWS AND REGULATIONS.

AND SPECIALIZED LAWMAKERS AREN'T ALWAYS VERY GOOD AT SEEING THE BIG PICTURE.

HAND ME THAT HAMMER.

LAWMAKERS ATTENTIVE TO PUBLIC OPINION CAN WIND UP CHASING IT.

THEY OVERREACT TO THE OUTRAGE OF THE MOMENT, VICTIMIZE WHOEVER IS UNPOPULAR TODAY, JACK UP PUNISHMENTS TO LOOK "TOUGH ON CRIME,"

AND THEN MOVE ON, LEAVING A MESS OF LAWS BEHIND THEM.

EVENTUALLY, THE LAW DOESN'T REFLECT SOCIETY SO WELL.

AND WE WIND UP IN MUCH THE SAME POSITION AS WE NOW FIND OURSELVES. THIS HAS HAPPENED THROUGHOUT HISTORY.

IT EVEN HAPPENED TO US BACK IN ANCIENT ROME!

OUR LAWS WERE OKAY FOR A WHILE...

WE TRIED TO BE **FAIR**, **PROTECTED** THE PEOPLE FROM THE SENATORS, AND NOT EVEN **RULERS** WERE ABOVE THE LAW.

(CORNELIUS TACITUS, ANNALS BOOK III)

BUT THEN OUR POLITICIANS STARTED TRYING TO BE *POPULAR* INSTEAD OF *PRINCIPLED*.

TO APPEASE THE MASSES, THEY WENT AFTER DISTINGUISHED CITIZENS...

...AS WELL AS UNPOPULAR *MINORITIES*.

(THAT'S NEVER HAPPENED IN YOUR ERA, RIGHT?)

IN RESPONSE TO UNIQUE CASES, VARIOUS PARTS OF GOVERNMENT ENACTED COUNTLESS LAWS THAT APPLIED TO EVERYBODY, AND OFTEN OVERLAPPED OR EVEN CONTRADICTED EACH OTHER.

THERE HAVE BEEN TOO MANY KILLINGS LATELY! **EVERYONE** IS ALLOWED TO USE WEAPONS TO PROTECT THEMSELVES FROM KILLERS AND THIEVES!

THERE HAVE BEEN TOO MANY KILLINGS LATELY! **NOBODY** IS ALLOWED TO CARRY ANY WEAPON WHATSOEVER WITHOUT A PERMIT FROM THE EMPEROR!

ABOUT 400 YEARS AFTER I WROTE ABOUT THIS, THE EMPEROR JUSTINIAN TRIED TO CONSOLIDATE ALL THOSE LAWS INTO A **SINGLE CODE**, A MERE 6,000 PAGES LONG.

IT WAS A MESS, I TELL YOU!

AND IT SEEMED THAT THE MORE **SCREWED** UP OUR GOVERNMENT WAS, THE MORE **LAWS** WE'D HAVE! *

* OR IN LATIN: "CORRUPTISSIMA REPUBLICA, PLURIMAE LEGES."

MUCH THE SAME THING HAPPENED IN MERRIE OLDE ENGLAND.

DON'T FORGET, YOU YANKS GOT YOUR LAWS FROM ME, ORIGINALLY! SO THIS IS RELEVANT.

WHEN ENGLAND · COALESCED IN · THE 900S, · ITS CRIMINAL LAW · WAS MOSTLY · A MATTER OF COMMON SENSE.

IT · STAYED · THAT WAY FOR ABOUT 500 · YEARS EVEN · DESPITE · THE NORMAN CONQUEST.

WHAT · PART OF "THOU SHALT · NOT STEAL" DIDN'T YOU · UNDERSTAND?

'**COURSE** IT'S COMMON SENSE! IT'S NOT AS IF SUCH RULES NEED TO BE WRITTEN IN **STONE**!

WELL, EXCEPT FOR THE TEN COMMANDMENTS, YEAH?

ALTHOUGH THE OCCASIONAL KING TOOK
A STAB OR TWO AT WRITING A CRIMINAL **CODE**,
EVEN THEN THEY DIDN'T BOTHER TRYING TO
EXPLAIN WHAT ANY OF IT **MEANT**.

OF COURSE NOT!
EVERYONE ALREADY
KNOWS WHAT
"MURDER" MEANS.
...DOLT.

AS A RESULT, CRIMINAL LAW WAS
FAIRLY **STRAIGHTFORWARD**.

"DON'T DISRESPECT
AUTHORITY, DON'T HURT
OTHER PEOPLE, AND DON'T
TAKE THEIR STUFF..."
YUP, THAT COVERS
EVERYTHING!

WELL, THERE WAS MORE TO IT THAN **THAT**.

EVEN IN MEDIEVAL TIMES,
THE ENGLISH ALREADY
HAD WELL-DEFINED
JUSTIFICATION
DEFENSES.

HAVE AT
YOU!

YOU
FIRST!

NO JURY
WOULD
CONVICT ME.

WHAT'S
A
JURY?

AND THEY APPLIED A RUDIMENTARY **MENS REA** TO ALL CRIMES.

MOTIVE DIDN'T MATTER, BUT CULPABILITY DID.

AND SO DURESS, INFANCY, AND INCAPACITY WERE ALL RECOGNIZED DEFENSES.

WE THOUGHT OF THIS STUFF **AGES** AGO!

PUNISHMENT WAS SIMPLE:

FOR MINOR OFFENSES, YOU PAID A **FINE.**

FOR MAJOR OFFENSES, YOU GOT HURT OR **KILLED.**

JAIL WASN'T REALLY USED SO MUCH AS A **PUNISHMENT** BACK THEN. IT WAS MOSTLY JUST A WAY TO MAKE SURE YOU STUCK AROUND LONG ENOUGH TO **BE** PUNISHED.

SOUNDS QUITE CIVILIZED!

CIVILIZED? NOT QUITE.

YOU SEE, ONE PREREQUISITE FOR A CIVILIZED SOCIETY IS WHAT'S CALLED *"THE RULE OF LAW."*

NEVER HEARD OF IT.

AND WHAT *RULED* IN THOSE DAYS WASN'T THE LAW, BUT *POWER.*

"NOBODY IS ABOVE THE LAW"? *HAW!* I NEEDED A GOOD LAUGH!

WHEN *MIGHT* MAKES RIGHT, YOU CAN'T *RELY* ON ANYTHING.

EXCUSE ME, GOOD SIR KNIGHT, BUT OUR CONTRACT SAYS YOU OWE ME TWELVE *MMMPH!*

YAWN

YOU AND WHAT ARMY?

BULLYING AND CORRUPTION MAKE LIFE JUST TOO *UNPREDICTABLE* FOR CIVILIZATION TO ADVANCE.

HEY, WANT TO INVEST IN SOME AWESOME ECONOMIC AND SOCIAL DEVELOPMENT?

FORGET IT. HOW LONG TILL THE RENAISSANCE?

WITHOUT THE RULE OF LAW, THE STATE ONLY RARELY GOT INVOLVED IN LAW ENFORCEMENT.

WHO NEEDED THE STATE? WE WERE ALLOWED TO PUNISH CRIMINALS *OURSELVES.*

BUT PERSONAL RETALIATION OFTEN LED TO REVENGE, FEUDS, AND EVEN THE OCCASIONAL PRIVATE WAR.

NOTHING TO SEE HERE!

AROUND 1400 OR SO, HOWEVER, THE *STATE* STARTED TO TAKE OVER CRIMINAL LAW AND LAW ENFORCEMENT.

IT STARTED OFF SMALL, WITH LAWS THAT, FOR THE FIRST TIME EVER, ACTUALLY DEFINED THE *ELEMENTS* OF PARTICULAR OFFENSES.

BUT ONCE BEGUN, CHANGE NOW CAME *FAST.*

WITHIN 150 YEARS, ENGLAND HAD TRANSFORMED INTO A RULE-OF-LAW SOCIETY!

EVEN HENRY VIII, POPULARLY REMEMBERED AS SOMETHING OF A DESPOT, SINCERELY BELIEVED THAT THE KING WAS SUBORDINATE TO THE LAW.

I MAY NOT LIKE IT, BUT THE LAW RULES ME, NOT THE OTHER WAY AROUND.

THIS WAS **HUGE!**

IS THAT A CRACK AT MY WEIGHT?

NOW, **NOBODY** WAS ABOVE THE LAW.

THIS WAS GREAT FOR SOCIETY, BUT IT WAS ALSO GREAT FOR THE LAW ITSELF.

ALL OF A SUDDEN, THE LAW HAD **POWER.**

AND YOU'D BETTER BELIEVE WE USED IT!

OVER THE NEXT 200 YEARS, THE POWERS THAT BE PASSED MORE AND MORE *LAWS*, DEFINING MORE AND MORE *CRIMES.*

(AND WITH THE KING GIVING WAY TO PARLIAMENT, THERE WERE MORE AND MORE POWERS THAT BE.)

THE COURTS (SEVERAL DIFFERENT KINDS) ALSO CREATED LAW.

THEY CONTRIVED A WHOLE HODGEPODGE OF WRITS AND RULES, DEFINING STILL *MORE* CAUSES OF ACTION.

AND THE COMPLEXITIES OF AN INDUSTRIALIZING, GLOBALIZING EMPIRE DEMANDED *BUREAUCRACY* TO MANAGE IT ALL.

INDUSTRIALIZATION BEGAT MANY NEW THINGS — AMONG THEM THE *"CRIME WAVE."* LAWMAKERS REACTED BY PASSING EVEN *MORE* LAWS.

(THE PUNISHMENTS, HOWEVER, STAYED MUCH THE SAME: EITHER A SLAP ON THE WRIST OR EXECUTION.)

OVER-REACTIONS IS MORE LIKE IT.

IN OUR HASTE, WE MADE OUR LAWS FAR TOO SWEEPING, WITH PENALTIES FAR TOO SEVERE.

WE HAD OVER **200** CRIMES WITH THE **DEATH PENALTY**, INCLUDING STUPID, PETTY NONSENSE LIKE:

DEFACING ANOTHER'S CLOTHES, PICKPOCKETING MORE THAN A SHILLING, THREATENING ASSAULT, GAY SEX, POACHING, UNLAWFUL ASSEMBLY, FIGHTING IN PUBLIC, SAYING BAD THINGS ABOUT THE KING, DAMAGING A SILK LOOM, CUTTING TREES, PETTY SHOPLIFTING...

BLACKSTONE HAD SOME INTERESTING IDEAS:

HARSHER PENALTIES DON'T DETER ANYONE. ALL THAT'S NEEDED FOR DETERRENCE IS THE MERE THREAT OF **SOME** PUNISHMENT.

SEVERE SENTENCES FOR MINOR OFFENSES HAVE ONLY LED TO **CONTEMPT** FOR THE LAW.

THAT ONLY LEADS TO MORE **CRIME**.

SO BLACKSTONE CALLED FOR REFORM:

GET RID OF LAWS PASSED OUT OF AMBITION OR REVENGE.

GET RID OF LAWS THAT WEREN'T MEANT TO APPLY TO EVERYONE.

GET RID OF PUNISHMENTS THAT ARE TOO SEVERE.

MOST OF ALL, GET RID OF LAWS THAT HAVE NOTHING TO DO WITH WHAT CRIMINAL LAW IS SUPPOSED TO BE FOR!

BLACKSTONE WAS AN INFLUENTIAL GUY, BUT *INERTIA* CAN BE EVEN MORE POWERFUL.

ENGLAND JUST WASN'T READY TO OVERHAUL ITS CRIMINAL LAW SO *DRASTICALLY.*

BUT WE WILL TAKE YOUR SUGGESTIONS UNDER ADVISEMENT.

ACROSS THE POND, HOWEVER,
THE NEWLY INDEPENDENT **UNITED STATES**
LISTENED HARD TO WHAT BLACKSTONE
(AND OTHERS LIKE HIM) HAD TO SAY.

*WE'RE WRITING
OUR LAWS
PRACTICALLY
FROM
SCRATCH!*

*MIGHT AS WELL
TRY TO GET
THEM RIGHT THE
FIRST TIME!*

THESE WEREN'T BACKWOODS HICKS.
THEY WERE EDUCATED MEN CAREFULLY
TRYING TO PUT THEIR ENLIGHTENMENT
PHILOSOPHIES INTO EFFECT.

AS EACH NEW STATE **EXPERIMENTED** WITH ITS OWN PRINCIPLED LAWMAKING, SOME SURPRISING THINGS STARTED TO HAPPEN.

FOR EXAMPLE, THE VERY CONCEPT OF CRIME SUDDENLY...

...CHANGED!

POW

OW!

FOR THE FIRST TIME, PERHAPS EVER, CRIME WAS BEING SEEN NOT AS AN OFFENSE AGAINST THE VICTIM, BUT STRICTLY AS AN OFFENSE AGAINST THE **STATE!**

DID YOU JUST...

HIT...?

ME?

ALSO, FOR THE FIRST TIME EVER, LEGAL MINDS WERE EXPLICITLY FIGURING OUT ALL THE DIFFERENT LEVELS OF CRIMINAL INTENT AND CULPABILITY, AND WHAT THEY **MEANT.**

THOUGH WE WOULDN'T **REALLY** GET THERE UNTIL THE 1950s.

AND WE DIDN'T YET FOCUS SO MUCH ON WHAT **WAS** GOING ON IN YOUR MIND, AS ON WHAT SOMEONE IN YOUR SHOES **MUST** HAVE BEEN THINKING.

MEANWHILE, BLACKSTONE'S UTILITARIAN EMPHASIS ON **DETERRENCE**, RATHER THAN ON RETALIATION, BECAME THE DRIVING FORCE OF ENLIGHTENED THOUGHT ON PUNISHMENT.

THE PURPOSE OF CRIMINAL LAW IS TO PROTECT **SOCIETY**, NOT TO SPANK THE WRONGDOER.

AND THEY SHARPLY **REDUCED** THE NUMBER OF CAPITAL (DEATH PENALTY) OFFENSES.

THEY'RE INSISTING THAT PUNISHMENT BE PROPORTIONATE TO THE OFFENSE?

SO MUCH FOR JOB SECURITY.

THIS FOCUS ON **DETERRENCE** AND **PROPORTIONALITY** GAVE RISE TO A WHOLE NEW KIND OF PUNISHMENT.

FAREWELL TO BRANDING, WHIPPING, AND THE PILLORY!

SAY HELLO TO **PRISON!**

PRISON SENTENCES COULD BE **CALCULATED** AND ADJUSTED TO JUST THE RIGHT **LENGTH** TO MATCH THE OFFENSE, AND TO DETER OTHERS.

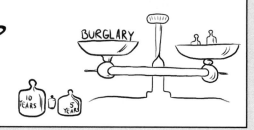

AND PRISON ALSO SERVED A REVOLUTIONARY NEW CONCEPT.

REHABILITATION!

THAT'S RIGHT, YOU'LL GET SOME PEACE AND QUIET TO REFLECT ON WHAT YOU'VE DONE WRONG.

AND YOU'LL COME BACK A BETTER PERSON FOR IT!

BEFORE THE CIVIL WAR, HOWEVER, THESE REFORMS WERE PURELY *THEORETICAL* FOR A LOT OF PEOPLE. GOVERNMENT DIDN'T PLAY MUCH OF A ROLE IN EVERYDAY LIFE.

SO IN MOST PLACES, CRIMINAL LAW HAD *REVERTED* BACK TO BEING ENFORCED BY THE LOCAL COMMUNITY, NOT BY THE STATE.

AND IN AREAS FAR FROM GOVERNMENT INTRUSION, PEOPLE CONTINUED TO TAKE THE LAW INTO THEIR OWN HANDS FOR A LONG TIME AFTER THAT.

(APPALACHIAN FEUDS, 1870s)

(WESTERN VIGILANTES, 1880s)

(SOUTHERN LYNCHINGS, 1920s AND BEYOND)

YOU COULD SAY IT WASN'T UNTIL THE 1930s THAT THE WHOLE UNITED STATES WAS, AT LEAST FOR THE MOST PART, A TRUE "RULE-OF-LAW" SOCIETY.

OUR FIRST POLICE FORCES WERE INTENDED MOSTLY TO CONTROL "MOB JUSTICE," RATHER THAN TO FIGHT CRIME.

THE LAW'S ASCENDANCY COINCIDED WITH THE RISE OF THE FEDERAL GOVERNMENT'S POWER.

TO MAKE A LONG STORY SHORT, THINK OF U.S. POLITICAL HISTORY AS A THREE-WAY TUG OF WAR FOR SOVEREIGNTY.

WE'RE IN CHARGE!

WE'RE IN CHARGE!

ESPECIALLY AFTER THE GREAT DEPRESSION AND THE CIVIL RIGHTS MOVEMENT GOT THE FEDS RILED UP.

I'M IN CHARGE.

GOING BACK TO THE PRINCIPLED, ENLIGHTENED JURISTS, MEANWHILE, DURING THE 1800s, THEY CAME UP WITH A NEW PRINCIPLE: THE **STRICT LIABILITY** CRIME.

WHAT? HOW IS **THAT** PRINCIPLED?

WELL, IT WAS **KIND** OF PRINCIPLED, ANYWAY. THE IDEA WAS TO DETER AND PUNISH "PUBLIC INCONVENIENCES" WHERE KNOWLEDGE OR INTENT WOULD BE NIGH IMPOSSIBLE TO **PROVE.**

LIQUOR LAW VIOLATIONS, FOR EXAMPLE.

OR KEEPING KIDS OUT OF POOL HALLS.

BECAUSE YOUR "BADNESS" WAS NOT RELEVANT FOR STRICT LIABILITY, THESE CRIMES WERE STRICTLY LIMITED TO OFFENSES WITH **NO MORAL STIGMA.**

IT WAS OKAY, BECAUSE NOBODY WOULD THINK YOU WERE A BAD PERSON.

NO WORSE THAN GETTING A PARKING TICKET.

A WHAT?

SEE, WE WERE PRINCIPLED!

SURE, STRICT LIABILITY CRIMES WERE **RARE** AT FIRST, AND THEY WERE VERY, **VERY** LIGHTLY PUNISHED.

BUT AS TIMES CHANGED, LAWS CHANGED, AND PUNISHMENTS GOT WORSE AND **WORSE...**

...BUT THE STRICT LIABILITY STAYED THE SAME.

FOR INSTANCE, LOOK AT THE CRIME PEOPLE USUALLY THINK OF WHEN YOU MENTION STRICT CRIMINAL LIABILITY — "**STATUTORY RAPE.**"

FOR HUNDREDS OF YEARS, IT WAS A CRIME TO HAVE SEX WITH A GIRL BEFORE SHE REACHED **PUBERTY.**

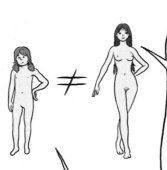

MENS REA WASN'T AN ISSUE, NOT BECAUSE OF ANY LEGAL POLICY, BUT BECAUSE IT SIMPLY NEVER CAME UP!

IN ALL THOSE CENTURIES, THERE IS NO RECORD OF A SINGLE PERSON RAISING EVEN A **MISTAKE** DEFENSE.

BECAUSE COME ON, HOW COULD YOU NOT KNOW?

BUT DURING THE VICTORIAN "NEW PRUDISHNESS" AFTER THE CIVIL WAR, STATES STARTED RAISING THE "AGE OF CONSENT" UP INTO THE **LATE TEENS!**

IF ANYONE ASKS, THE **THEORY** IS THAT "AS A MATTER OF LAW" (REMEMBER THAT PHRASE?) THE TEEN **COULDN'T** HAVE CONSENTED. AND SEX WITHOUT CONSENT IS RAPE.

BUT NOW IT COULD BE VERY EASY TO **MISTAKE** WHETHER A PARTICULAR YOUNG WOMAN IS "OF AGE."

HOW OLD **YOU** THOUGHT SHE WAS ISN'T THE IMPORTANT FACTOR HERE.

THEN WHAT IS?

SOMEONE SLEPT WITH MY DAUGHTER, THAT'S WHAT!

BUT THIS "AS A MATTER OF LAW" EXPLANATION WASN'T THOUGHT UP UNTIL DECADES LATER.

ONCE STRICT LIABILITY WAS RECOGNIZED AS A LEGITIMATE PRINCIPLE, IT WAS ONLY A MATTER OF TIME BEFORE IT WOULD BE APPLIED TO A VARIETY OF CRIMES.

YOUR BLOOD ALCOHOL WAS 0.084%.

HOW THE HECK COULD I HAVE KNOWN *THAT?*

THAT TURTLE CAME FROM NEW YORK.

HOW THE HECK COULD I HAVE *KNOWN* THAT?

YOUR EMPLOYEE DIDN'T FILE THE RIGHT FORM.

HOW THE HECK COULD I HAVE KNOWN THAT?

REGULATORY OFFENSES, ONCE RESERVED FOR ALCOHOL AND PUBLIC DANGERS, REALLY BEGAN TO EXPLODE IN NUMBER.

(STARTING, IRONICALLY ENOUGH, DURING THE REAGAN ADMINISTRATION.)

AND AGAIN, A HUGE NUMBER OF THESE HAVE BEEN STRICT LIABILITY CRIMES.

AND THE PENALTIES BEGAN TO **SKYROCKET.**

ALL THESE STRICT LIABILITY CRIMES USED TO HAVE MINIMAL PUNISHMENTS, AND NO SOCIAL STIGMA, REMEMBER?

BUT NOT ANYMORE.
FOR EXAMPLE:

DRUNK DRIVING?
USED TO BE A TRAFFIC FINE, MAYBE LOSE YOUR LICENSE.

NOW IT COULD MEAN JAIL, AND CERTAINLY HEAVY STIGMA.

AND STATUTORY RAPE?
IT USED TO BE PUNISHED VERY LIGHTLY. REMEMBER, THE POINT WAS MORE TO CONTROL DAUGHTERS THAN TO PUNISH SONS — AND ONLY EXCEPTIONAL CASES WERE SEEN AS REALLY "BAD."

BUT NOW? NOW IT'S A HEINOUS, EVIL SEX CRIME, WITH SEVERE PRISON SENTENCES FOLLOWED BY DECADES ON A SEX OFFENDER REGISTRY. AND THE STIGMA COULDN'T BE WORSE.

THESE REFLECT LEGITIMATE CHANGES IN SOCIETY'S ATTITUDES.

THE PROBLEM IS THAT WHEN THE PUNISHMENTS WENT UP, MENS REA GOT LEFT BEHIND.

VAGUENESS, OVERBREADTH AND EXCESSIVE PUNISHMENT REARED THEIR UGLY HEADS IN THE "GET TOUGH ON CRIME" LAWS THAT STARTED BACK IN THE 1970s.

WAR ON CRIME — WAR ON DRUGS
SCHOOL CRIMES — CYBER CRIMES — HATE CRIMES
SEX CRIMES — WAR ON TERRORISM

RESULTING IN LAWS LIKE THE COMPUTER FRAUD AND ABUSE ACT,* WHERE NOBODY REALLY KNOWS WHAT'S PROHIBITED.

UNTIL THEY GET PROSECUTED FOR IT, OF COURSE.

*AMONG OTHERS.

AND RESULTING IN SKY-HIGH SENTENCES FOR LOW-LEVEL DRUG DEALERS.

AND SCAPEGOATS BEING PROSECUTED TO APPEASE PUBLIC OPINION.

AND FOOLISH RULES WITH SEVERE PENALTIES.

AND PUNISHMENTS IN GENERAL JUST RATCHETING UP HIGHER AND HIGHER...

HEY, WE HAVE TO LOOK GOOD SOMEHOW!

AND EVERYTHING ELSE THAT TACITUS AND BLACKSTONE COMPLAINED ABOUT BACK IN THEIR OWN TIMES.

AND THAT'S HOW WE END UP WITH TRUDY AND DENNIS.

GOOD PEOPLE, WHO NEVER MEANT TO DO ANYTHING WRONG.

AND WHO ARE NOW GOING TO PRISON.

WHEN **ANYONE** CAN BE PROSECUTED, JUSTICE BECOMES A **LOTTERY**.

I KNOW YOU WERE ONLY KEEPING UP WITH TRAFFIC.

YOU'RE JUST THE ONE I **HAPPENED** TO PULL OVER.

BUT THE FACT THAT WE'VE BEEN HERE BEFORE MAKES IT EASIER TO SEE HOW TO **FIX** THINGS BEFORE THEY GET TOO OUT OF HAND.

AND THE FIXES ARE **EASY**:

ONLY LET **ELECTED** REPRESENTATIVES ENACT CRIMINAL LAWS.

HAVE A **DEFAULT** MENS REA LIKE "KNOWINGLY," FOR LAWS THAT LEFT ONE OUT.

RESTORE THE OLD RULE THAT **VAGUE** LAWS MUST ALWAYS BE INTERPRETED IN FAVOR OF THE **ACCUSED**.

ENACT A "**COMMON SENSE**" RULE TO PROTECT PEOPLE SWEPT UP BY OVERBROAD LAWS.

BUT IN THE MEANTIME,
LET'S JUST KEEP OUR HEADS DOWN
AND GO OVER SOME OF THE DIFFERENT
TYPES OF CRIMES...

"PUTTING IT ALL TOGETHER"

AT JACK'S PARTY LAST WEEK,
LIGHT-FINGERED LAUREL FELL IN LOVE
WITH JACK'S CRUMMY OLD VIOLIN.

THAT'D LOOK SO
MUCH BETTER IN MY
LIVING ROOM!

SO SHE
TOOK IT HOME
WITH HER.

LAUREL GOT *CAUGHT,* AND NOW SHE'S IN TROUBLE.

PERFECT!

LET'S PUT TOGETHER WHAT WE'VE LEARNED SO FAR AND SEE IF WE CAN TELL WHAT *CRIME* LAUREL COMMITTED.

BURGLARY?

ROBBERY?

WARNING:
EVERY STATE'S LAW IS DIFFERENT. THESE ARE JUST EXAMPLES. DON'T THINK THEY APPLY TO YOU IN REAL LIFE.

THAT SAID, LET'S LOOK AT THE **BURGLARY** STATUTE IN LAUREL'S STATE:

A person commits burglary when he knowingly enters a dwelling without permission, and does so with the intent to commit a crime inside.

BUT I **HAD** JACK'S PERMISSION TO BE THERE — HE INVITED ME!

THAT'S **ALL** WE NEED TO KNOW.

ALL IT TAKES IS FOR ONE ELEMENT TO BE FALSE FOR US TO KNOW THAT THE CRIME WASN'T COMMITTED.

WE DON'T EVEN NEED TO ASK WHETHER SHE INTENDED TO STEAL ANYTHING WHEN SHE WENT INSIDE.

LAUREL DID **NOT** COMMIT BURGLARY.

WHEW!

NOW LET'S CHECK TO SEE IF SHE COMMITTED **ROBBERY**.

HERE'S THE **ROBBERY** STATUTE IN LAUREL'S STATE:

A person commits robbery when he intentionally takes another's property without permission, and does so by using or threatening to use force.

NO, NOT **THE FORCE**, JUST FORCE.

THE FIRST ELEMENT SEEMS TO BE SATISFIED.

LAUREL CERTAINLY TOOK JACK'S VIOLIN ON PURPOSE, AND SHE DIDN'T HAVE HIS PERMISSION TO DO SO.

 UH OH.

BUT ROBBERY IS **MORE** THAN MERE THEFT.

THINK "**MUGGING.**"

LAUREL DIDN'T USE OR THREATEN ANY FORCE. SHE JUST SNUCK OUT WITH THE FIDDLE. SO SHE DIDN'T COMMIT ROBBERY, EITHER.

SO WHAT **DID** SHE COMMIT?

IN LAUREL'S STATE, NON-VIOLENT THEFT IS CALLED "*LARCENY.*" HERE'S THE STATUTE:

A person commits the misdemeanor of petty larceny when, with the intent to deprive another of some property, he takes that property without permission.

A person commits the felony of grand larceny when, with the intent to deprive another of some property, he takes that property without permission, and the property is worth more than five thousand dollars.

WE KNOW LAUREL *TOOK* JACK'S VIOLIN, RIGHT?

RIGHT...

AND SHE DIDN'T HAVE HIS *PERMISSION,* DID SHE?

NO...

AND SHE MEANT TO KEEP IT FOR *HERSELF*?*

UH HUH...

OR OTHERWISE KEEP IT FROM JACK.

WE HAVE A WINNER!

LAUREL HAS COMMITTED **PETTY** LARCENY.

BUT LET'S MAKE SURE THAT'S ALL.

DID SHE ALSO COMMIT **GRAND** LARCENY?

NAH, THAT CRUMMY OLD VIOLIN ISN'T WORTH ANYTHING.

ACTUALLY, IT'S A COLLECTOR'S ITEM! THAT VIOLIN IS WORTH FORTY THOUSAND DOLLARS!

WHAT!?

BUT I HAD NO WAY OF **KNOWING** THAT!

JACK

THAT WAS A MISTAKE OF FACT! ISN'T THAT A **DEFENSE**?

SORRY, LAUREL, BUT NO. MISTAKE ONLY HELPS YOU IF IT **NEGATES** AN ELEMENT OF THE CRIME. THIS STATUTE DOESN'T **CARE** WHETHER YOU KNEW THE VIOLIN'S VALUE.

ANYWAY, EVEN IF THE VIOLIN **WAS** AS WORTHLESS AS YOU THOUGHT, YOUR ACT WAS STILL A **CRIME**.

IN MANY STATES, THAT **ALONE** IS ENOUGH TO PRECLUDE ANY DEFENSE OF MISTAKE.

THE VIOLIN WAS WORTH MORE THAN FIVE GRAND. SO UNDER HER STATE'S LAW, LAUREL COMMITTED **GRAND LARCENY**.

SAY GOODBYE, LAUREL.

LATER.

SEE HOW THAT WORKED? PRETTY EASY, RIGHT?

LET'S TRY AGAIN, THIS TIME WITH SOMETHING
A LITTLE MORE... *VIOLENT.*

AT THE GAME LAST WEEK, AL REACHED OUT
TO ORDER A BEER JUST AS FRED WAS
LEANING FORWARD TO CHEER AND...

THAT'S ALL THAT HAPPENED. NOW THE D.A. IS TRYING TO DECIDE **WHOM** TO CHARGE WITH **WHAT.**

HERE'S THE **BATTERY** STATUTE IN THEIR STATE:

One commits the misdemeanor of battery when one intentionally or recklessly causes bodily harm to another person.

One commits the felony of aggravated battery when one intentionally or recklessly causes severe bodily harm or disfigurement of another person, or when one intentionally or recklessly causes any bodily harm to another person with a deadly weapon.

OKAY, FIRST WHAT DID **AL** DO?

HE BROKE BY DOZE!

BUT IT WAS AN ACCIDENT!

WELL, IT WASN'T **INTENTIONAL.** AND "**RECKLESS**" MEANS YOU WERE AWARE THAT YOU **COULD** HAVE HURT SOMEONE, BUT DID IT **ANYWAY...**

I DON'T SEE THAT HERE. IT WAS JUST AN **ACCIDENT.**

THE ISSUE FOR ME IS WHETHER YOU COMMITTED SIMPLE BATTERY, OR AGGRAVATED BATTERY.

YOU DIDN'T USE A WEAPON, SO THE QUESTION IS WHETHER AL'S INJURIES COUNT AS "SEVERE" OR NOT.

THERE'S SOME BRUISING, BUT NOTHING BROKEN, NO DAMAGED ORGANS OR ANY REAL DISFIGUREMENT, SO I'M CALLING THIS A MISDEMEANOR BATTERY.

I GUESS I CAN LIVE WITH THAT.

WAIT, I'M NOT DONE YET.

NOW I HAVE TO DECIDE WHETHER TO CHARGE IT AS A HATE CRIME.

A **WHAT!?**

A "**HATE CRIME**" LAW TYPICALLY PUNISHES YOU **MORE** SEVERELY FOR A CRIME WHEN YOU DID IT NOT BECAUSE OF **WHO** THE VICTIM WAS, BUT **WHAT** HE WAS.

*NOTE: FICTIONAL PROSECUTOR. YOUR MILEAGE MAY VARY.

NOW LET'S TALK ABOUT **RAPE.**

MEET FIONA.

AW, NO WAY.
I'M OUTTA
HERE.

OKAY...
LET'S MEET STACY.

WHAT?
NUH UH.

THEN HOW ABOUT WE...

HOW ABOUT **NOT.**

FINE.

HERE'S STICKIE McSTICKFIGURE.

DARN.
I MEAN,
HI.

AND HERE IS THE RAPE LAW IN HER JURISDICTION:

A person commits second-degree rape when he or she knowingly engages in sexual intercourse with another person without that other person's consent.

A person commits first-degree rape by using physical force to compel another person to engage in sexual intercourse with him or her.

A person is presumed not to give consent when he or she is mentally incapacitated or physically helpless.

NOW LET'S SEE WHAT HAPPENED TO STICKIE.

DARN.
I MEAN....

DARN.

EARL GRABBED STICKIE IN A DARK ALLEY, PUT A GUN TO HER HEAD, AND THREATENED TO **KILL** HER IF SHE MADE A SOUND.

THEN HE LIFTED HER DRESS AND STARTED TO SHOVE **HIS** SEX ORGAN INSIDE **HERS.**

A POLICEMAN **IMMEDIATELY** RAN UP AND ARRESTED HIM.

EARL COMMITTED **RAPE ONE.**

NO I DIDN'T. I NEVER **FINISHED** THE ACT.

THAT DOESN'T MATTER.
ANY PENETRATION, NO MATTER HOW SLIGHT, COUNTS AS SEXUAL INTERCOURSE.

BUT SHE NEVER SAID "NO." HOW DO YOU KNOW SHE DIDN'T CONSENT?

ANY TIME YOU USE FORCE TO **COMPEL** SOMEONE TO HAVE SEX, AS A MATTER OF LAW THEY DID NOT CONSENT.

SHE DIDN'T **HAVE** TO SAY NO; IT WAS PERFECTLY OBVIOUS.

EARL'S GOING TO PRISON.

SAY GOODBYE, EARL.

WHATEV...

EASY, RIGHT? LET'S TRY ANOTHER.

JEFF WAS AT A BAR ONE NIGHT, WHEN HE NOTICED THAT STICKIE HAD *ALREADY* HAD ONE TOO MANY DRINKS.

SO HE BOUGHT HER SOME *MORE*.

DON'T MIND IF I DO!

STICKIE HAD A *GREAT* TIME, AND SOON WAS BEYOND BLOTTO.

JEFF TOOK HER BACK TO HIS PLACE, THEY MADE OUT, AND HE *ASKED* IF SHE WANTED TO DO IT.

OKAY!

THEN THEY *DID* IT.

JEFF COMMITTED *RAPE TWO*.

NO WAY, MAN. SHE SAID *YES*.

NOPE, THAT DIDN'T COUNT.

WHA HUH?

SHE WAS **FAR** TOO DRUNK FOR HER "OKAY" TO HAVE BEEN LEGALLY **EFFECTIVE.**

IT DIDN'T COUNT AS CONSENT.

BUT... BUT...

IT DIDN'T COUNT BECAUSE YOU **KNEW** SHE WAS TOO DRUNK TO KNOW WHAT SHE WAS DOING. WHAT'S WORSE, YOU MADE HER THAT DRUNK ON **PURPOSE.**

IF YOU HADN'T KNOWN YOURSELF THAT SHE WAS INCAPABLE OF GIVING LEGALLY EFFECTIVE CONSENT, YOU'D HAVE A DEFENSE HERE.

BUT YOU **KNEW.** SO IT'S RAPE TWO.

SAY GOODBYE, JEFF.

BUT THEN THERE WAS THE TIME BACK WHEN STICKIE WAS DATING HUBERT.

AFTER THEIR FOURTH OR FIFTH DATE, THEY WERE HAPPILY MAKING OUT, ONE THING LED TO ANOTHER, AND...

OH MY!

THE THING IS, STICKIE REALLY DIDN'T WANT TO HAVE SEX WITH HUBERT THEN.

I JUST WASN'T READY. I DIDN'T *AGREE* TO IT, IT JUST, Y'KNOW.... *HAPPENED.*

BUT ALTHOUGH SHE DIDN'T *CONSENT*, NEITHER DID SHE SAY OR DO ANYTHING THAT WOULD HAVE LET HUBERT *KNOW* IT.

HOW WAS I SUPPOSED TO KNOW?

YOU COULDN'T HAVE KNOWN, SO EVEN THOUGH THIS WASN'T CONSENSUAL, IT *WASN'T* RAPE.

YOU'RE FREE TO GO, HUBERT.

WHEN IT COMES TO RAPE, THE ELEMENTS ARE EASY. WHAT CAN BE HARD IS PROVING WHAT REALLY HAPPENED.

FOR EXAMPLE, THERE WAS THE TIME WHEN STICKIE MET BARTHOLOMEW AT A PARTY.

THEY SANG, THEY DANCED, THEY HAD A BLAST.

AND THE NEXT MORNING, SHE WOKE UP IN HIS BED.

OH NO.

A FEW DAYS LATER, HER FRIEND TRIXIE ASKED ABOUT IT.

BARTHOLOMEW SAYS YOU GUYS HOOKED UP.

SO, DETAILS?

NO! I MEAN, I DIDN'T **WANT** TO DO IT.

TRIXIE CALLED THE COPS, AND NOW THE PROSECUTOR HAS TO DECIDE WHETHER TO CHARGE BARTHOLOMEW WITH RAPE.

NO FORCE IS ALLEGED, SO I'M ONLY LOOKING AT RAPE TWO.

THAT STILL LEAVES A FEW POSSIBILITIES...

1. SHE DIDN'T CONSENT, AND HE KNEW IT.

2. SHE DIDN'T CONSENT, BUT HE DIDN'T KNOW.

3. SHE DID CONSENT.

THAT SOUNDS A LITTLE "HE SAID, SHE SAID."

HOW DO YOU DECIDE?

IT CAN BE A TOUGH CALL. MOSTLY, IT'S GOING TO COME DOWN TO WHO STRIKES ME AS MORE **CREDIBLE**. I'LL WEIGH WHAT FACTS I HAVE, BUT I'LL LISTEN TO MY GUT, TOO.

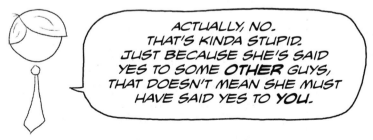

THE LAW USED TO LET YOU USE A WOMAN'S SEXUAL PAST TO DISPROVE A PRESENT CLAIM OF RAPE. BUT THAT'S ANCIENT HISTORY. FOR DECADES NOW, EVERY U.S. JURISDICTION HAS HAD ONE FORM OR ANOTHER OF WHAT'S CALLED A *"RAPE SHIELD LAW,"* WHICH LIMITS OR PREVENTS THE USE OF PRIOR SEXUAL BEHAVIOR TO PROVE PRESENT CONSENT.

IN THIS STATE, YOU WOULD BE ALLOWED TO BRING UP THAT THE TWO OF YOU HAD A SEXUAL **RELATIONSHIP**, TO SHOW CONSENT...

BUT YOU TWO ONLY JUST MET, SO YOU CAN'T EVEN SAY THAT.

WHAT **ELSE** HAVE YOU GOT?

HOW ABOUT THE FACT THAT STICKIE NEVER WENT TO THE COPS? SHE ONLY TOLD A FRIEND.

WELL, YOU DO SEE THAT WHEN A WOMAN HAS MADE A FALSE ACCUSATION, PERHAPS BECAUSE OF REGRET...

OMIGOD, WHAT HAVE I DONE?

HIV?

PREGNANT?

PEOPLE WILL DESPISE ME!

UNLESS...

UNLESS IT WASN'T REALLY MY FAULT.

...WHERE THE WOMAN ISN'T SO MUCH TRYING TO GET THE GUY IN TROUBLE, AS TRYING NOT TO BE HELD **RESPONSIBLE** FOR THE ACT.

BUT WOMEN WHO **HAVE** BEEN RAPED DON'T ALWAYS REPORT IT TO THE POLICE.

IT'S **ONE** THING TO CONSIDER FOR SURE, BUT IT WON'T BE THE DECIDING FACTOR.

(AND BTW, I'M NOT SEEING OTHER INDICIA OF A FALSE ACCUSATION, LIKE REVENGE OR EMOTIONAL INSTABILITY.)

IT'S NOT GOING TO BE EASY, BUT I'M JUST GOING TO HAVE A LOOK AT ALL THE EVIDENCE AND DECIDE WHAT I BELIEVE... AND WHAT I CAN PROVE.

WELL, NOW THEY'RE GETTING INTO ISSUES OF CRIMINAL PROCEDURE AND EVIDENCE, SO LET'S MOVE ON.

SAY GOODBYE, BARTHOLOMEW.

SAY **GOODBYE**, STICKIE.

GOD, I HATE YOU.

NOT EVERY CRIMINAL STATUTE IS AS SIMPLE
AS THE ONES WE'VE DISCUSSED SO FAR.

FOR EXAMPLE, THE *HOMICIDE* STATUTE IN
THE (FICTIONAL) STATE OF FREMONT
LOOKS SOMETHING LIKE THIS:

A person commits <u>Murder in the First Degree</u>
when he:
1. Intends to kill a police officer or witness to
   a crime, and causes the death of any person; OR
2. Intends to kill another person, and causes
   the death of that person in a cruel and depraved
   manner; OR
3. Commits a violent act with the intent to achieve
   a political end, and so causes the death of any
   person.

A person commits <u>Murder in the Second Degree</u>
when he:
1. Intends to kill another person, and causes the
   death of any person; OR
2. Recklessly, and without concern for risk to
   human life, causes the death of any person; OR
3. Participates in a felony that posed a risk of
   physical danger to another person, and during
   the commission of the crime or flight therefrom
   any person is killed by any participant in the
   crime or by any person attempting to prevent the
   crime or flight therefrom.

A person commits <u>Manslaughter in the First Degree</u>
when he:
1. Intentionally causes the death of another
   person, but successfully asserts a defense of
   provocation; OR
2. Intends to seriously injure another person, and
   causes the death of any person.

HANG ON, THIS IS SUPPOSED TO BE AN *ILLUSTRATED* GUIDE, REMEMBER? WHAT'S WITH THE WALL OF TEXT?

JUST A COUPLE MORE SECTIONS. AND NOTE, BY THE WAY, THAT MOST HOMICIDE STATUTES ARE *FAR* MORE COMPLICATED THAN EVEN THIS. SO, MOVING ON:

A person commits <u>Manslaughter in the Second Degree</u> when he recklessly causes the death of another person.

A person commits <u>Criminally Negligent Homicide</u> when he negligently causes the death of another person, and his negligence was a significant departure from a reasonable standard of care.

GOT ALL THAT? GREAT, NOW LET'S SEE WHAT IT ALL MEANS.

GIORGIO THOUGHT HIS WIFE LUANNE WAS *CHEATING* ON HIM. SO HE CAME HOME FROM WORK EARLY ONE DAY, AND WAITED FOR HER IN THE KITCHEN.

WHEN SHE CAME HOME, HE STARTED SCREAMING AND YELLING AT HER. SHE SCREAMED AND YELLED RIGHT BACK.

IN HIS RAGE, GIORGIO THREW A PLATE AT LUANNE.

SHE FELL *HARD*, RIGHT ONTO A BOTTLE.

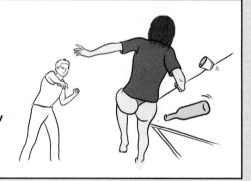

THE GLASS SHATTERED UNDER HER ARMPIT, AND A SHARP EDGE TORE OPEN HER BRACHIAL ARTERY.

GIORGIO CALLED AN AMBULANCE, BUT LUANNE BLED TO DEATH LONG BEFORE IT ARRIVED.

SO, IN THE FICTIONAL STATE OF FREMONT, WHAT CRIME (IF ANY) DID GIORGIO COMMIT?

HE *MURDERED* MY LITTLE GIRL!

NO! IT WAS JUST AN *ACCIDENT!*

WHOA... WHOA... **WHOA!** FIRST THINGS FIRST. AND THE *FIRST* ISSUE IS WHETHER WE HAVE AN ACTUS REUS.

IN OTHER WORDS, DID GIORGIO **CAUSE** LUANNE'S DEATH?

NOT DIRECTLY. HE DIDN'T CUT HER ARMPIT HIMSELF. THERE WAS A **SERIES** OF EVENTS THAT RESULTED IN HER DEATH.

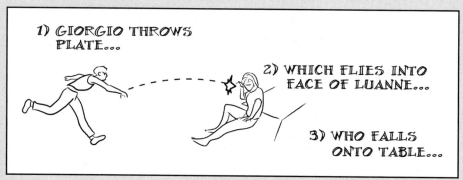

1) GIORGIO THROWS PLATE...

2) WHICH FLIES INTO FACE OF LUANNE...

3) WHO FALLS ONTO TABLE...

4) THEN ONTO BOTTLE...

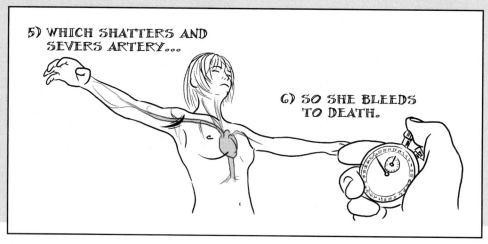

5) WHICH SHATTERS AND SEVERS ARTERY...

6) SO SHE BLEEDS TO DEATH.

LUANNE CERTAINLY WOULD NOT BE DEAD IF GIORGIO HADN'T THROWN THAT PLATE AT HER, SO THAT WAS A "*CAUSE IN FACT.*"

(REMEMBER ALL THIS?)

NOW WE ASK IF IT WAS A "*PROXIMATE CAUSE*," WHICH JUST MEANS "CLOSELY RELATED ENOUGH TO COUNT."

MANY STATES HAVE A "*MISDEMEANOR MANSLAUGHTER*" RULE THAT CAN CUT THROUGH ALL THIS. IN SUCH STATES, SO LONG AS GIORGIO WAS DOING ANYTHING UNLAWFUL AND SHE DIED, HE'D BE GUILTY OF AN INVOLUNTARY MANSLAUGHTER.

HERE, THROWING THE PLATE WAS AN UNLAWFUL BATTERY, SO IN THOSE STATES GIORGIO WOULD BE GUILTY UNDER A MISDEMEANOR MANSLAUGHTER RULE.

THE FICTIONAL STATE OF FREMONT *DOESN'T* HAVE A RULE LIKE THAT, SO WE HAVE TO ASK HOW *PREDICTABLE* IT WAS THAT THROWING A PLATE AT LUANNE COULD HAVE RESULTED IN HER DEATH.

OKAY, YEAH, THAT'S A FREAKIN' HEAVY PLATE.

IF IT HAD SMASHED HER IN THE FACE, AT THE VERY LEAST IT WOULD HAVE BUSTED SOME BONES. MAJOR BRAIN TRAUMA AND EVEN DEATH WOULDN'T HAVE BEEN OUT OF THE QUESTION.

BUT IT DIDN'T! THE **PLATE** ISN'T WHAT KILLED HER, IT WAS THE **BOTTLE**.

THE BOTTLE WASN'T **PREDICTABLE.**

(PROSECUTOR, HERE.)

SORRY, GIORGIO. IT **WAS** PREDICTABLE THAT YOUR ACT COULD HAVE KILLED HER, AND IT WAS ALL PART OF THE SAME INCIDENT.

JUST BECAUSE IT WASN'T THE PLATE ITSELF THAT KILLED HER, IT WAS ALL RELATED **ENOUGH** TO BE PROXIMATE CAUSE.

SO THERE WAS **CAUSATION.** YOU CAUSED LUANNE'S DEATH. THAT TAKES CARE OF ACTUS REUS.

SO NOW LET'S DETERMINE YOUR **MENS REA**, TO SEE WHICH KIND OF HOMICIDE YOU COMMITTED HERE.

I DIDN'T **HAVE** ANY MENS REA! I WASN'T TRYING TO KILL HER, IT WAS AN **ACCIDENT!**

I **BELIEVE** YOU WEREN'T TRYING TO KILL LUANNE, BUT THAT'S NOT THE **ONLY** MENS REA.

IF YOU WERE SO RECKLESS THAT YOU DIDN'T **CARE** IF IT KILLED HER, THAT'S PRETTY DEPRAVED. YOU'D BE LOOKING AT MURDER TWO HERE.

IT DIDN'T EVEN OCCUR TO ME THAT SHE COULD HAVE DIED!

AGAIN, STOP GETTING AHEAD OF ME HERE. YOU WERE TRYING TO BUST HER *FACE* WITH THAT PLATE...

AND YOU CAUSED HER *DEATH*.

THAT'S MANSLAUGHTER IN THE *FIRST* DEGREE.

REMEMBER HOW THIS WORKS? GIORGIO COULD REDUCE THE CHARGE (BUT ONLY REDUCE IT) IF:

1. LUANNE PROVOKED HIM,
2. INTO A PASSION THAT OVERCAME HIS REASON,
3. HE KILLED IN THE HEAT OF THAT PASSION, **AND**
4. A REASONABLE PERSON (THE JURY) WOULD HAVE DONE THE SAME THING IN THAT SITUATION.

MOVING ON...

JON RAN TO TELL HIS BUDDIES
WHAT HE'D JUST OVERHEARD.

WHILE STEVIE WENT OFF TO PRACTICE HER DRIVING...

ARCHIE WAS KILLED **INSTANTLY** WHEN THE BAT HIT HIM.

JON TOOK A LITTLE **LONGER,** BUT HE DIED THAT NIGHT.

AND NOW STEVIE IS ABOUT TO BE ARRESTED FOR **MURDER.**

WHAT?

BUT *I* DIDN'T KILL ANYONE.

NOPE, BUT AS A MATTER OF LAW, YOU'RE *RESPONSIBLE.*

YOU ALL BROKE INTO A STORE, WITH A GUN, AND PEOPLE GOT KILLED AS A RESULT?

EVERYONE WHO TOOK PART IN THE CRIME IS RESPONSIBLE.

THAT'S CALLED *"FELONY MURDER"* AND IN THIS STATE THAT'S MURDER TWO.

SAYS SO RIGHT IN THE STATUTE. ARCHIE WAS KILLED DURING THE *COMMISSION* OF THE CRIME, AND JON WAS KILLED DURING THE *FLIGHT* THEREFROM.

STILL, AT THE VERY LEAST YOU'RE GONNA BE CHARGED WITH THE FELONY MURDER OF ARCHIE.

DOESN'T MATTER IF THE VICTIM WAS ONE OF THE **CROOKS** OR JUST A BYSTANDER.

SO SAY **GOODBYE**, STEVIE.

ONE FINAL EXAMPLE,
AND WE SHOULD BE GOOD TO GO:

MEET CHUCK.

GO TO HELL.

CHUCK IS **REALLY** ANGRY AT THE GOVERNMENT.

THEY TAKE MY MONEY, AND GIVE IT TO **FREELOADERS.**

THEY IGNORE MY VOTE, AND KOWTOW TO **CORPORATE** MONEY.

THEY PROTECT CRIMINALS, AND **PERSECUTE** FOLKS LIKE ME.

IT'S TIME FOR A **REVOLUTION!**

LIKE MANY BEFORE HIM, CHUCK HAS DECIDED TO USE VIOLENCE AND FEAR TO GET THE CHANGES HE WANTS.

TIMOTHY MCVEIGH

KU KLUX KLAN

ALEXANDER BERKMAN

TED "UNABOMBER" KACZYNSKI

CHARLES MANSON

LEON CZOLGOSZ

JOHN ALLEN MUHAMMAD

ANTHRAX– LETTER GUY

WEATHERMEN

JOHN BROWN (?)

THE FACT THAT IT RARELY ACTUALLY **WORKS** DOESN'T SEEM TO HAVE OCCURRED TO HIM.

AND SO HE PLANTED A BOMB AT THE FREMONT STATE CAPITOL, WITH THE TIMER SET TO GO OFF AT 3 A.M.

I'M NOT **TRYING** TO KILL ANYONE...

BUT STILL, Y'KNOW?

AROUND 10 P.M., WHILE STROLLING PAST THE CAPITOL, KEVIN ASKED CYNDI TO STOP FOR A MOMENT.

THE POLICE QUICKLY TRACED THE EXPLOSIVES TO CHUCK AND **ARRESTED** HIM. HE'S BEEN CHARGED WITH A VARIETY OF CRIMES RELATED TO PLANTING HIS BOMB INSIDE THE BUILDING. BUT WHAT ABOUT KEVIN AND CYNDI'S **DEATHS**? HOW SHOULD HE BE CHARGED FOR THAT?

REMEMBER THE AXES OF **EVIL**? MENS REA ISN'T THE ONLY THING THAT AFFECTS THE SEVERITY OF AN OFFENSE.

IN THIS STATE, TERRORISM IS CONSIDERED SO **WICKED** THAT EVEN IF SOMEONE DIES BY ACCIDENT, IT'S STILL PUNISHED AS FIRST-DEGREE **MURDER.**

LET'S GO THROUGH THE ELEMENTS OF THE CRIME.
I'D SAY PLANTING THAT BOMB COUNTS AS A **VIOLENT** ACT.

A person commits Murder in the First Degree when he:
1) commits a violent act,
2) with the intent to achieve a political end,
3) and so causes the death of any person.

AND CHUCK WAS TRYING TO SCARE THE GOVERNMENT INTO CHANGING ITS POLICY, SO HE CLEARLY INTENDED TO ACHIEVE A **POLITICAL** GOAL.

AND PEOPLE DIED AS A RESULT.

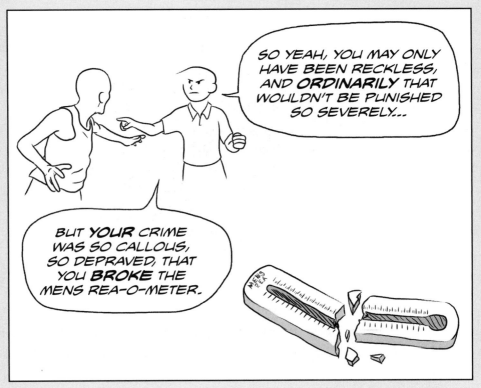

SO YEAH, YOU MAY ONLY HAVE BEEN RECKLESS, AND *ORDINARILY* THAT WOULDN'T BE PUNISHED SO SEVERELY...

BUT *YOUR* CRIME WAS SO CALLOUS, SO DEPRAVED, THAT YOU *BROKE* THE MENS REA-O-METER.

AND SO, INSTEAD OF BEING PUNISHED FOR THE MISDEMEANOR OF MANSLAUGHTER TWO, CHUCK IS FACING THE MOST *SEVERE* PUNISHMENT THE FICTIONAL STATE OF FREMONT *ALLOWS.*

AND...

THAT'S *IT*, REALLY, FOR CRIMINAL LAW.

NEEDLESS TO SAY, I HOPE YOU *NEVER*
NEED TO USE *ANY* OF THIS.

BUT WITH THAT, LET'S SAY
GOODBYE TO CRIMINAL LAW
AND GET READY FOR OUR NEXT SUBJECT:
CRIMINAL PROCEDURE.

MIRANDA WARNINGS, SEARCH AND SEIZURE,
INDICTMENTS, TRIALS, PROSECUTORS,
DEFENSE ATTORNEYS, SENTENCING...

IT'LL BE FUN!

BE SURE TO VISIT *LAWCOMIC.NET*
TO CATCH THE LATEST
INSTALLMENTS.

SEE YOU THERE,
NATHAN

Acknowledgements

Obviously, none of the information in this book came off the top of my head. It was taught to me, by many patient professors, bosses, and colleagues. A complete list would take up many pages, but at the top would be (in chronological order) Mike Seidman, Silas Wasserstrom, Carter Phillips, Allen Applbaum, Wally Mlyniec, Kristin Henning, Peter Kougasian, Matt Menchel, Pat Dugan, Ellen Biben, Eric Seidel, Barry Ginsberg, Gordon Mehler, and Bruce Barket. To the extent I got anything right, they deserve all the credit. Any errors are my own.

I have to thank my wife Rebecca for her forbearance as this went from "just a quick doodle or two on my lunch hour" into a full-time second job, with me hogging her computer and Wacom tablet on nights and weekends. For not wincing too hard when I'd proudly show her my amateurish scribbles. For her helpful criticism ("augh, not those mitten hands again"; "that's not how boobs work, you know"; "hmm... no, see you ought to... no"). And for her never-ending wonderful support, encouragement, and cheerleading throughout.

Special thanks go to Jason Wilson, master of the publishing universe, who was insane enough to take on such an unusual project; to Jack Arthur, graphic designer par excellence, who worked tirelessly to convert my vertical-scrolling web images into something that actually looked good on paper; and of course to Scott Greenfield, who not only had the original idea to turn this into a book, but convinced the rest of us that he was right.

And I have to thank all of the followers, forwarders, rebloggers, and redditors who spread the word. Your astonishing good looks are eclipsed only by your awesomeness. But you already knew that.